Contents

SECTIONS

AIRCRAFT TYPE COLOR KEY

- Bombers
- Cargo
- Commercial / Passenger
- Fighters
- First Aircraft
- General Aviation
- Homebuilt
- Observation / Reconnaissance
- Spacecraft
- Trainers

NOTE: Actual display locations of aircraft may vary from those pictured since the printing of this book.

This book is dedicated to the volunteers who selflessly give their time to the Museum each week. You are the Museum's lifeblood, and your stories, experiences and personalities bring our aircraft to life. The Evergreen Aviation & Space Museum would not be what it is today without your tireless efforts and loyal dedication. You are truly the heart and soul of our Museum.

**The Evergreen Aviation & Space Museum and
The Captain Michael King Smith Educational Institute's mission is**
*to inspire and educate,
to promote and preserve aviation and space history,
to honor the patriotic service of our veterans.*

Top: The Spruce Goose *slowly makes its way up the Willamette River, heading to Portland, Oregon.*

Above: The Aviation Museum at night.

Right: Captain Michael King Smith

Captain Michael King Smith

The Evergreen Aviation & Space Museum and The Captain Michael King Smith Educational Institute is dedicated to the life and memory of Museum Founder, Captain Michael King Smith, son of Evergreen International Aviation's founder, Mr. Delford M. Smith.

Michael Smith graduated from McMinnville High School as an honor student, senior class president and an Eagle Scout. Graduating from the University of Washington in 1989, he received a commission in the U.S. Air Force as a Second Lieutenant.

He graduated first in his class from Columbus Air Force Base with an undergraduate degree in pilot training and received many awards including the Commander's Trophy, Distinguished Graduate and Flying Excellence. In 1991, he graduated from Fighter Lead-In Training School at Holloman Air Force Base and from F-15 RTU (Replacement Training Unit) at Tyndall Air Force Base.

During his military career, Captain Smith made considerable contributions to the field of aviation in Oregon. An

outstanding pilot, he flew lead in his F-15 *Eagle* fighter plane for the 123rd Fighter Squadron, the "Redhawks," with the Oregon Air National Guard.

Michael strived to build a place that would inspire and educate today's youth, honor our veterans and preserve aviation artifacts with dignity. His dream was realized with the Evergreen Aviation & Space Museum.

MUSEUM HISTORY

The Evergreen Aviation & Space Museum prides itself on a mission of education. From our two separate Aviation and Space Museum buildings filled with educational and inspiring craft and exhibits, to our Theater showing movies with educational content, to the Wings & Waves Waterpark and its many informative and educational aspects—we prove that learning and fun can go hand-in-hand.

The glimmer in the eye.

The ah-ha moment.

The burst of understanding.

The Evergreen Museum Campus doesn't just teach. We inspire students of all ages by providing the spark to get kids interested in the sciences. As an aerospace museum and waterpark, students are immersed in hands-on activities that teach fun and informative lessons about science, technology, engineering and math. Our various programs, tours and classes offer a wide range of educational opportunities for individuals and groups of all ages.

Students between the ages of 12 and 18 can learn more by joining our team and becoming an Evergreen Discovery Ambassador. Younger students (grades K-3rd) can get an early start by joining our Aerospace Book Club. Educational groups can also enjoy a more immersive experience by spending

> ## To those who love aviation, the sky is home. "
>
> — Anonymous

a night at the Museum, camping at Evergreen's Oak Grove Camping Area, or joining our Summer Camp program. Our Scouting program also offers opportunities to earn aviation and space merit badges.

Teachers and group leaders can arrange educational tours for their classes, which have access to all of our exhibits, from hands-on demonstrations to more than 200 planes and spacecraft. Individuals can explore our Home School and Educational Outreach programs.

We strive to provide quality educational films in our Theater that not only showcase staggering visuals, but also provide educational value to the students who are watching them.

Always striving to offer the most comprehensive experience possible, the Evergreen Aviation and Space Museum has partnered

with several organizations. We value our educational partners. These partnerships allow us to expand our educational reach and offer exciting new programs, while also making a valuable contribution to our community.

Our partnership with McMinnville High School provides hands-on educational opportunities to their Engineering and Aerospace Sciences Academy (EASA), while our partnership with Chemeketa Community College enhances their current offerings. We also offer exciting programs in conjunction with the Civil Air Patrol, and the FIRST Robotics Leagues.

We are fortunate and thankful to have the support of the community in our quest to "inspire and educate, to promote and preserve aviation and space history, and to honor the patriotic service of our veterans."

Early Flight

Since before recorded history, humans have looked to the sky and dreamed of flying free like the birds. While a few brave pioneers were able to go aloft in balloons or gliders, it was on the windswept dunes of Kitty Hawk, on December 17, 1903, that the dream became a reality. The Wright Brothers and their success with the first controllable, sustained, powered flight opened up a new age for humanity. Within 20 years, the airplane would go from a flimsy machine capable of a few moments in the air to an angel of mercy and industrial workhorse for both commerce and warfare.

Wright 1903 *Flyer* Replica

Contrary to the belief that Orville and Wilbur Wright were simple Dayton, Ohio bicycle mechanics who stumbled upon a successful design, the 1903 *Flyer*'s brief flights were the product of more than four years of intensive study and careful calculations. The brothers constructed a wind tunnel, and designed and flew many full-size gliders; questioning theories that had been accepted for years before adopting a working solution. Their first experiments began with kites in 1899, but it was on December 17, 1903, that they achieved their dream when the *Flyer* struggled into the air from its launching rail, with Orville at the controls. The 12-second hop of 120 feet, into a 27-mile per hour headwind, went down in history as the world's first powered, controlled and sustained airplane flight.

Like most of the Wright's previous test gliders, the 1903 *Flyer* was built from spruce and ash wood with a muslin cloth covering, but it featured a four cylinder engine of the Wright's own design turning two propellers. What was really unique was its form of control.

The pilot lay down upon a cradle on the lower wing, controlling the elevator with his left hand. Turns were accomplished by moving the cradle with his hips, which pulled cables, causing the wings to twist and the rudders to move. These changes caused the *Flyer* to bank much like a bicyclist does in a turn, which was the key to controlling the aircraft.

The *Flyer* did not last long. Piloted alternately by both brothers, three more flights were made that day. As it sat parked in the sand, a gust of wind tumbled the craft. It was smashed

EARLY FLIGHT

Above: Orville Wright (left) and his elder brother Wilbur.

Right: The first flight by the Wright Brothers at Kitty Hawk, North Carolina, December 17, 1903.

beyond practical repair, and never flown again. The remains were crated up and returned to Dayton before eventually being displayed at the Massachusetts Institute of Technology and later the Science Museum in London, England. Only in 1948 did it return to the U.S., after a long-standing feud with the Smithsonian (who backed Samuel Langley as the first to build an aircraft capable of flight) was resolved. The *Flyer* has remained there ever since, having undergone a major restoration in 1985 to arrest corrosion and deterioration of the fabric.

The 1903 Wright *Flyer* replica was built by Century Aviation in Wenatchee, Washington. Accurate in almost every way, this replica was built from copies of plans made in 1985 by the National Air & Space Museum.

Specifications

Type:	Experimental
First Flight:	December 17, 1903
Wingspan:	40 feet, 4 inches
Length:	21 feet, 1 inch
Height:	9 feet
Power:	One Wright 4-cylinder water-cooled engine
Crew:	1
Top Speed:	30 miles per hour

EARLY FLIGHT

Blériot XI *Racer* Replica

In the early years of aviation, pilots often vied for prizes offered for accomplishing great feats of airmanship. One of those prizes was offered by the London *Daily Mail* to the first to cross the English Channel. On the morning of July 25, 1909, French aviator Louis Blériot made aviation history by crossing the Channel in an aircraft of his own design, the Blériot XI.

The wood and fabric monoplane, powered by a 25 horsepower Anzani engine, could barely reach 300 feet above the waves. Despite fog, rain and strong winds, Blériot flew by dead-reckoning and eventually made a hard landing in a Dover farm field 37 minutes after leaving France. Blériot became an instant celebrity and his Model XI went on to become one of the world's first mass-produced aircraft.

Created by Jack Lenhardt and Evergreen restoration volunteers using original plans, this *Racer* is a replica that was completed and flown in 2006. It is powered by a Rotax engine that is far more reliable than the original Anzani engine.

Specifications

Type:	Sport / Touring / Trainer
First Flight:	January 23, 1909
Wingspan:	25 feet, 7 inches
Length:	25 feet
Height:	8 feet, 10 inches
Power:	One Anzani 3-cylinder air-cooled engine
Crew:	1
Top Speed:	47 miles per hour

EARLY FLIGHT

■ **Curtiss** JN-4 *Jenny* (*Canuck*) Replica

The Curtiss *Jenny* (*Canuck*) holds a special place in the hearts of American flyers, as it was the most produced U.S. aircraft in the World War I era. Its nickname, *Jenny*, came from its Curtiss designation as the Model JN.

Roughly 95 percent of U.S. and Canadian pilots trained in a JN-4 during World War I. After the war, there was a surplus of planes and young men who knew how to fly, giving rise to "barnstorming." Barnstormers traveled across America selling rides and performing stunts.

This replica was built from 1999 to 2001 by Century Aviation in Washington, with many original JN-4 pieces, including an original Curtiss OX-5 engine and vintage metal parts. This aircraft represents a *Canuck*, a Canadian version of the Curtiss *Jenny* used to train both Canadian and American pilots. Though essentially the same as American JN-4s, the *Canuck* has a few different physical features, such as rounded vertical and horizontal stabilizers; strut-connected ailerons on both wings; and the absence of notches in the wings that aided pilot visibility.

Type:	Trainer
First Flight:	July 1916
Wingspan:	43 feet, 7 inches
Length:	27 feet, 2 inches
Height:	9 feet, 11 inches
Power:	One Curtiss OX-5 liquid-cooled engine
Crew:	1-2
Top Speed:	74 miles per hour

EARLY FLIGHT

Curtiss Model D "Headless" Pusher Replica

Specifications

One of the most successful competitors to the Wright Brothers was Glenn Curtiss. Like the Wrights, his designs were "pushers," with the engine mounted behind the pilot, although he utilized a more intuitive control system.

Curtiss developed ailerons; small "winglets" mounted between the upper and lower wing that could be moved to change airflow. To control pitch, the pilot pushed or pulled the control wheel to operate the plane's elevator. With the ailerons wired to his seat, the pilot simply leaned to one side to bank in that direction, while the rudder was operated by turning the control wheel. Unlike most Curtiss pushers, this example had its elevator moved to the rear and is known as a "Headless" pusher.

A Navy Curtiss Model D flown by Eugene Ely made the first takeoff from a ship in 1910 and the first landing on a ship in 1911, giving rise to what would someday be the aircraft carrier.

This replica is on loan from the Hiller Aviation Museum.

Type:	Sport / Observation
First Flight:	1911
Wingspan:	38 feet, 3 inches
Length:	29 feet, 3 inches
Height:	9 feet
Power:	One Curtiss E-4 liquid-cooled cooled engine
Crew:	1
Top Speed:	50 miles per hour

EARLY FLIGHT

de Havilland DH-4M-1

Specifications

Type:	Bomber / Reconnaissance
First Flight:	August 1916
Wingspan:	42 feet, 5 inches
Length:	29 feet, 11 inches
Height:	9 feet, 8 inches
Power:	One Liberty L-12 liquid-cooled engine
Crew:	1-2
Top Speed:	118 miles per hour

Nicknamed "Flaming Coffins" for the alleged ease with which they caught fire, the DH-4 was a British-designed World War I observation and bombing plane.

When the U.S. entered the war, it had no warplane designs of its own and built nearly 5,000 DH-4s under license. The DH-4 was the only American-made airplane used in combat during World War I. After the war, DH-4s continued to be the backbone of U.S. air power, serving until 1932.

After being passed through a series of civilian owners, this DH-4 was sold to Paramount Pictures and appeared in the 1938 movie *Men with Wings*. Famous movie pilot Paul Mantz flew stunts for the movie, and in 1941, he purchased the aircraft. The plane also appeared in *The Court Martial of Billy Mitchell* (1955), as well as *Spirit of St. Louis* (1957) starring Jimmy Stewart.

Mantz was killed while filming the final flight scenes of the movie *Flight of the Phoenix* (1966), and the DH-4 was sold at auction the same year. It was later purchased by Evergreen in 1990.

EARLY FLIGHT

Leonardo DaVinci's *Ornithopter* Replica

Recognized as one of the great creative geniuses of all time, Leonardo DaVinci was a true "Renaissance man" who experimented in the worlds of painting, sculpture, anatomy, science and engineering. Beginning in 1485, Leonardo began working to solve the age-old riddle of how birds flew. Over the next 20 years he studied all nature of flying creatures including birds, bats and insects to see how their wings functioned. Based on those studies he created complex designs for flying machines that would allow humans to fly like birds.

It is not known if Leonardo ever attempted to build or fly his flapping-wing "Ornithopter." If he had, his attempt would not have been successful because the *Ornithopter* did not incorporate any features that we now know are needed for lift; and the coordination of arm, leg and head movements needed to fly the craft are far beyond human capacity.

This replica of Leonardo's *Ornithopter* was built by Ken Spence of Bend, Oregon.

Specifications

Type:	Human Powered Aircraft
First Flight:	Unknown
Wingspan:	21 feet
Length:	4 feet, 7 inches
Height:	6 feet, 1 inch
Power:	One human being
Capacity:	1
Top Speed:	Unknown

EARLY FLIGHT

Fokker Dr.1 Triplane Replica

World War I pilots saw themselves as individuals fighting above the death-filled trenches, and they used their aircraft as canvases on which to paint their standards. One of the most famous was a German named Manfred von Richtofen; the "Red Baron" who flew a blood red colored Fokker Dr.1 Triplane.

Designed to counter the Sopwiths that were dominating the Western front in early 1917, prototypes of the Dr.1 were given to von Richtofen to test in combat. Elated with its speed and maneuverability, he quickly downed two Allied aircraft in two days and urged that fighter squadrons be equipped with the Triplane as soon as possible. The Red Baron eventually scored 20 of his 80 aerial victories in a Dr.1 before his death in combat. The aircraft was not without faults, and failures of the wings claimed many lives before newer types like the Fokker D.VII replaced it.

This 3/4 scale replica was built in 1964 and flown for more than 40 years before being donated to the Museum.

Specifications

Type:	Fighter
First Flight:	July 5, 1917
Wingspan:	23 feet, 7 inches
Length:	18 feet, 11 inches
Height:	9 feet, 8 inches
Power:	One Oberursel UR.II 9-cylinder rotary engine
Crew:	1
Top Speed:	115 miles per hour

EARLY FLIGHT

Nieuport 11 *Bébé* Replica

In the winter of 1916 the air over the European battlefield was controlled by the Germans and their Fokker monoplanes but the "Fokker Scourge" was soon to end with the appearance of the Nieuport 11. Allied pilots flying the fast, nimble Nieuports were able to outperform the Fokkers with their superior maneuverability and quickly even the score. However, the superiority would not last. Within three months, the Nieuport 11 was being replaced by the more powerful Nieuport 17 and the Spad VII in Allied air forces.

Nicknamed the "Bébé" or Baby, the Nieuport 11 was a not a true biplane, but rather a sesquiplane, with a full upper wing and a half-span lower wing. Unfortunately, the lower wing was weaker and occasionally failed under high-stress maneuvers, with fatal results.

This 7/8 scale replica was built by the father and son team of Jerrold and Zack Stevens. It is finished in the markings of the Lafayette Escadrille, a squadron of American pilots flying for the French in World War I before the U.S.'s official entry into the war.

Specifications

Type:	Fighter
First Flight:	January 5, 1916
Wingspan:	24 feet, 9 inches
Length:	19 feet
Height:	7 feet, 10.5 inches
Power:	One LeRhone 9C 9-cylinder rotary engine
Crew:	1
Top Speed:	97 miles per hour

EARLY FLIGHT

Sopwith *Camel* F.1 Replica

In the deadly spiral of advancing technology that ruled World War I aviation, the Sopwith Company endeavored to create a bigger, faster and more heavily armed version of its Pup fighter to counter the German Albatros fighters. The result was regarded as the finest British fighter of World War I, the nimble Sopwith *Camel* that shot down more enemy aircraft than any other World War I fighter. A skilled pilot could quickly make a kill thanks to the *Camel*'s amazing maneuverability, but for the unwary pilot, the *Camel*'s vicious handling qualities could be deadly.

Many famous Allied aces including Victoria Cross winner William Barker flew the *Camel*, but perhaps the most well known was Capt. A.R. Brown, who is credited with shooting down Manfred von Richthofen, the "Red Baron." By the end of the war, *Camel*s equipped 58 British and five American squadrons.

This replica *Camel* was built from original plans and includes many original components. It is on loan from the Rinaldi family of Eugene, Oregon.

Specifications

Type:	Fighter
First Flight:	December 22, 1916
Wingspan:	26 feet, 11 inches
Length:	18 feet, 9 inches
Height:	8 feet, 6 inches
Power:	One Clerget 9B 9-cylinder rotary engine
Crew:	1
Top Speed:	115 miles per hour

EARLY FLIGHT

AVIATION TIMELINE

1903	1906	1908	1909	1911

December 17, 1903

Orville Wright makes the first powered, sustained, and controlled heavier-than-air flight in the Wrights' *Flyer* for 12 seconds at Kitty Hawk, North Carolina.

November 12, 1906

Alberto Santos-Dumont, a Brazilian, makes the first successful powered flight in Europe in the *Santos-Dumont 14-bis*. Santos-Dumont travels a distance of 722 feet in 21 seconds near Château de Bagatelle, France.

July 4, 1908

Glenn H. Curtiss makes the first official public flight in the United States. He flies 5,080 feet, winning the Scientific American Trophy and its $2,500 prize.

July 25, 1909

Louis Blériot makes the first airplane crossing of the English Channel. He crossed in his Blériot Type XI from Les Barraques, France to Northfall Meadow, England in 37 minutes.

September 17, 1911

Calbraith P. Rodgers makes the first transcontinental flight across the United States. He flies from Sheepshead Bay, New York to Pasadena, California in 49 days. The trip requires 69 stops.

EARLY FLIGHT

1912

1913

1914

1916

1919

April 16, 1912

Harriet Quimby, the first American woman to become a licensed pilot, crosses the English Channel, becoming the first woman to do so. Flying in a Blériot monoplane loaned from Louis Blériot, she flew 59 minutes from Dover, England to Hardelot, France.

May 13, 1913

Igor Sikorsky builds and test-pilots the first four-engine airplane, the S-21 *Russky Vityaz*.

January 1, 1914

Tony Jannus pilots the first regularly scheduled airline service in the United States. He flies a Benoist XIV flying boat from St. Petersburg to Tampa, Florida.

September 17, 1916

Germany's Manfred von Richthofen, or the Red Baron, makes his first confirmed kill. Considered the ace-of-aces of World War I, Richthofen will be officially credited with 80 air combat victories, more than any other pilot at the time.

June 14, 1919

John Alcock and Arthur Whitten Brown, British aviators, make the first non-stop transatlantic flight. Flying in a modified World War I Vickers Vimy bomber, they travel from St. John's, Newfoundland, to Clifden, Ireland.

The Golden Age

The second 20 years of aviation has often been called "the Golden Age," and in truth it was. Young men who learned to fly in World War I barnstormed their way across the country in surplus airplanes, selling rides and giving many their first close-up look at a flying machine. The rise of air mail service and airlines helped to move people and goods across the continents at a faster rate, having a direct impact on how people did business. At the same time, aviation created a new group of heroes, such as Charles Lindbergh, Amelia Earhart and Douglas "Wrong-Way" Corrigan, all who became household names due to their daring feats of flying.

Ford *Tri-Motor* 5AT-B

Many people know of Ford's Model T, nicknamed the "Tin Lizzie," but most have forgotten that the Ford name also flew on the corrugated metal wings of the "Tin Goose." With three powerful motors, all-metal construction and the most trusted name in transportation on the side, the *Tri-Motor* was popular with many airlines.

Having brought the automobile to the masses, Henry Ford was looking to expand his operations when inventor and airplane builder William Stout approached Ford's son Edsel in 1923

with a proposal for a new single-engine airliner. Inspired by the designs of Hugo Junkers in World War I, Stout proposed an aircraft with a corrugated metal skin, for strength and durability. Ford bought out Stout, adapted the design to fit three engines for greater reliability, and the *Tri-Motor* was born. It was an advanced design for its time, although it shared many traits with Ford automobiles, being relatively inexpensive, reliable and simple to maintain.

The early days of airline service were far from luxurious. With their luggage

stowed in the wings, passengers had to be tough, as the ride was bumpy and the plane was so loud that the stewardess passed out cotton for ear plugs. Some flyers, chilled by the cold air at higher altitudes, complained that the *Tri-Motor* should be called the "Flying Icebox." And perhaps worst of all, Fords flew low, bumping and bouncing their way through turbulent skies, making air sickness a common affliction. Still, it ushered in the age of air transport and gave many airlines their start.

In addition to the airline market, the

THE GOLDEN AGE

Ford *Tri-Motor* found work with the military, flying with the U.S. Army, Navy and Marines, as well as the air forces of seven other countries. Admiral Richard Byrd selected the *Tri-Motor* for his first successful flight over the South Pole in 1929. Johnson Air Service (acquired by Evergreen in 1975) even utilized *Tri-Motor*s for dropping smokejumpers into wild fires from the 1930s through the 70s.

Built in 1928, this Ford was delivered to Transcontinental Air Transport, the forerunner to TWA, and flew passengers between San Diego and New York. It later found its way to Mexico where it was re-skinned without the corrugation. Purchased by Harrah's in Reno during the 1970s, it was restored to its original condition, before being acquired by Evergreen in 1990.

Specifications

Type:	Airliner
First Flight:	June 11, 1926
Wingspan:	77 feet, 10 inches
Length:	50 feet, 3 inches
Height:	12 feet, 8 inches
Power:	Three Pratt & Whitney R-985 Wasp C-1 radial engines
Crew:	3
Capacity:	9-12 passengers
Top Speed:	115 miles per hour

THE GOLDEN AGE

Beechcraft D17A *Traveler*

The Model 17, commonly called the *Staggerwing*, was the first aircraft produced by the Beech Aircraft Company. Starting in 1932, more than 780 Beechcraft 17s were produced over 17 years. The Model 17 gets its unique nickname *Staggerwing* because of its unusual arrangement of wings. Most biplanes, the upper wing is located farther forward than the lower, but that is reversed on the *Staggerwing*.

This 1939 Beechcraft D17A *Staggerwing*, is the last known surviving example of the A-model. It is also the

first of eight D17As built. Designated as the only UC-43F, this aircraft was the only A-model to serve in World War II. In 1943, the aircraft was delivered to the Civil Aeronautics Administration (CAA) in Texas, and later flew with the Alamo Airline Service. Rumor has it that Winston Churchill flew in it during his Idaho fishing trip.

The aircraft changed hands many times until 1989, when Alan and Rebecca DeBoer of Ashland, Oregon acquired it. In 2001, the DeBoers donated it to the Museum.

Type:	General Aviation / Military Transport
First Flight:	November 4, 1932
Wingspan:	32 feet
Length:	26 feet, 7.8 inches
Height:	8 feet, 6 inches
Power:	One Wright R-760 radial engine
Crew:	1
Capacity:	4 passengers
Top Speed:	186 miles per hour

THE GOLDEN AGE

Curtiss Model 51 *Fledgling*

The *Fledgling* was created by Curtiss in 1927 to meet a U.S. Navy requirement for a new trainer to teach "fledgling" aviators the basics of flight. Beating out 14 competitors, the *Fledgling* was put into mass production with over 50 being built. Its construction featured a steel-tube frame, an aluminum frame tail with wood frame wings; not much different from the *Jenny* it replaced.

Curtiss felt the design also had commercial potential, so they developed the Model 51 *Fledgling* in 1929, utilizing the unique Challenger radial engine of their own design. Unfortunately, the Great Depression caught up with Curtiss and only 109 were built. Most served with Curtiss' own air taxi service, resplendent in the company's signature orange and yellow paint scheme.

The Museum's *Fledgling* was the fifty-first one built and served its early years in St. Louis. After a stint in Alaska, it was acquired by Gene Burrill of Medford, Oregon in the 1960s. His widow, Gladys, donated it in July 2009. It was restored by Museum volunteers.

Type:	Trainer
First Flight:	1927
Wingspan:	39 feet, 2 inches
Length:	27 feet, 4 inches
Height:	10 feet, 4 inches
Power:	One Curtiss R-600 Challenger radial engine
Crew:	2
Top Speed:	109 miles per hour

THE GOLDEN AGE

Curtiss *Robin* B

The Curtiss *Robin* was the most successful general aviation aircraft of its time. Featuring simple, strong, steel tube and wood frame construction, and room for three, it easily outsold its competitors. Curtiss offered several possible engines, ranging from an OX-5 inline to a Challenger radial, to meet a customer's specific needs.

Several *Robin*s made highly publicized flights during the 1930s, including Douglas "Wrong-Way" Corrigan's journey from New York to Ireland in 1938. Corrigan declared his intention to fly to California, but instead crossed the Atlantic!

This *Robin* was built in 1929 for C.R. Putnam of Pontiac, Michigan. At the time, Putnam was one of the few instructors who willingly taught women to fly, including one who soloed on this aircraft and later became his wife. It was built with an OX-5 engine that was later replaced with a Challenger and later still with a Continental R670. It was donated to the Museum in 2004, and restored by Museum volunteers.

Specifications

Type:	Touring
First Flight:	August 7, 1928
Wingspan:	41 feet
Length:	25 feet, 1 inch
Height:	8 feet
Power:	One Continental R670 radial engine
Crew:	1
Capacity:	3 passengers
Top Speed:	120 miles per hour

THE GOLDEN AGE

Curtiss CW-A-22 *Falcon*

When Curtiss-Wright set out to design a new sport plane, they wanted it to be a popular civilian craft, as well as a successful military trainer. Created with traits from the CW-19 civil airplane and the CW-21 interceptor, the first CW-22 appeared as a sleek general aviation machine in 1940. However, with World War II looming, there was no civilian market and all its customers would be the military.

Improved versions went to Turkey, the Netherlands East Indies and other countries, but most were acquired by the U.S. Navy under the designation SNC-1. Fitted with machine guns and practice bombs, *Falcon*s helped teach marksmanship for pilots and gunners, while others were used to teach navigation, instrument flying and radio communications.

This airplane is the first and only civilian CW-22 *Falcon* built. It was purchased by Stafford Lambert of St. Louis in 1939, and afterward went through a succession of owners in California and New Mexico. It was acquired by Evergreen in 1990.

Specifications

Type:	Sport / Trainer
First Flight:	January 1, 1940
Wingspan:	35 feet
Length:	27 feet
Height:	9 feet, 11 inches
Power:	One Wright R975-28 Whirlwind radial engine
Crew:	2
Top Speed:	198 miles per hour

THE GOLDEN AGE

Douglas DC-3A

The DC-3 is unquestionably one of the greatest airplanes ever built. First flown in airline service in 1936, many DC-3s are still flying today. Originally built as the DST (Douglas Sleeper Transport), the DC-3 instantly made every other passenger aircraft obsolete.

When the U.S. entered World War II, many civilian DC-3s were drafted into service to carry troops and cargo. Douglas also churned out a military version of the plane, the C-47 *Skytrain*.

This is the second oldest surviving Douglas DC-3, and it was delivered to United Air Lines in 1936. Named the "Mainliner Reno," it was also the first to be fitted with Pratt & Whitney supercharged engines. It has flown more than 15 million passenger miles; equivalent to 30 round-trips between the Earth and the moon. After restoration was completed in 1987, the plane performed in air shows across the U.S. The DC-3 was acquired by Evergreen in May 1990.

Specifications

Type:	Civilian Passenger / Cargo
First Flight:	December 17, 1935
Wingspan:	95 feet
Length:	64 feet, 5.5 inches
Height:	16 feet, 11 inches
Power:	Two Pratt & Whitney R-1830 radial engines
Crew:	2
Capacity:	32 passengers
Top Speed:	230 miles per hour

THE GOLDEN AGE

Granville Brothers E *Sportster* Replica

Specifications

The small, flashy Granville Brothers (Gee Bee) E *Sportster* embodies the spirit of sport aviation in the 1930s. Five brothers, led by Zantford Granville, went from building simple biplanes to producing highly advanced racers that set speed records.

Advertised as having no rivals in performance, maneuverability or beauty, the brothers marketed their *Sportster*s with a number of different engines for less than $5,000. Still, they could be challenging to fly, and all four of the Model E *Sportster*s were destroyed in crashes. While the Great Depression ruined hopes for mass production, much of the design for the famous R and Z racers came from these earlier *Sportster*s.

Scott Crosby of Antelope, California built this replica in 1987 using copies of original construction drawings, which he obtained from the National Air & Space Museum. Surviving several crashes, it was sold to Jim Teel who had Crosby's help in rebuilding it before donating it to the Museum.

Type:	Sport
First Flight:	1930
Wingspan:	25 feet
Length:	17 feet, 3 inches
Height:	8 feet
Power:	One Warner Super Scarab radial engine
Crew:	1
Top Speed:	148 miles per hour

THE GOLDEN AGE

■ **Piper** J-3C-65 *Cub*

It has been said that it's impossible to kill yourself flying a Piper *Cub*. While not exactly true, *Cub*s are simple to fly and forgiving of mistakes, which has endeared them to several generations of pilots. Developed from C. Gilbert Taylor's E-2 which first flew in 1930, the *Cub* was further refined by William Piper who bought Taylor out in 1936.

Piper's *Cub*s were basic, honest, small planes and became the trainers of choice for the Civilian Pilot Training Program, which trained thousands of pilots during World War II. It is estimated that over

80 percent of all World War II pilots got their first flight in a *Cub*. Many civilian *Cub*s were also employed for patrol duties with the newly formed Civil Air Patrol.

This *Cub* was one of 253 Piper training gliders built during World War II. Designated TG-8, it had an elongated nose, shorter gear, spoilers, and of course, no engine. After the war, many TG-8s were converted into powered *Cub*s, including this one. It is most likely the only "glider" *Cub* still in existence.

Specifications

Type:	Trainer
First Flight:	1938
Wingspan:	35 feet, 3 inches
Length:	22 feet, 5 inches
Height:	6 feet, 8 inches
Power:	One Continental A-65, four-cylinder air-cooled engine
Crew:	2
Top Speed:	87 miles per hour

THE GOLDEN AGE

Ryan NYP *Spirit of St. Louis* Replica

Probably no other flight in history, except for the Wright Brothers' first flight, did more to advance aviation than that of Charles Lindbergh in May 1927. Attempting to win the Otreig Prize, of $25,000 for the first non-stop flight between New York and Paris, Lindbergh was airborne for 33 hours and 30 minutes and succeeded where many before him had failed. The key to his success was a custom designed aircraft built by the Ryan Aeronautical Company that he named *The Spirit of St. Louis*.

Based on the earlier M-2 mail plane, the NYP (which stood for New York to Paris) was designed and built in 60 days. It featured a special self-lubricating engine and fuel tanks that held 450 gallons; enough to travel over 4,000 miles. The main tank was installed in front of the pilot, which meant that Lindbergh had no forward view and had to use a periscope to see where he was going.

This replica of the *Spirit of St. Louis* was built by Century Aviation of Wenatchee, Washington.

Specifications

Type:	Long Range Record Aircraft
First Flight:	April 28, 1927
Wingspan:	46 feet
Length:	27 feet, 7 inches
Height:	9 feet, 10 inches
Power:	One Wright J-5C Whirlwind radial engine
Crew:	1
Top Speed:	133 miles per hour

THE GOLDEN AGE

AVIATION TIMELINE

1921

1924

1926

1927

1928

June 15, 1921

Bessie Coleman becomes the first African American woman to receive an international pilot's license.

April 6, 1924

Four Douglas World Cruisers of the U.S. Army Air Corps take off from Seattle, Washington, to begin a six-month westbound journey that will culminate in the first round-the-world flight.

May 8, 1926

Flying a Fokker F-VII *Tri-motor*, navigator Richard E. Byrd and pilot Floyd Bennett of the United States make the first airplane flight over the North Pole. The flight takes 15.5 hours.

May 21, 1927

The American aviator Charles Lindbergh completes the first nonstop solo flight across the Atlantic Ocean. Departing from Garden City, New York, Lindbergh flies to Paris, France in 33.5 hours.

May 31, 1928

Charles Kingsford Smith, an Australian aviator, makes the first trans-Pacific flight from the United States to Australia. Flying from Oakland, California, Smith and his crew stop in Hawaii and Fiji en route to their final destination of Brisbane, Australia.

THE GOLDEN AGE

| 1929 | 1932 | 1933 | 1937 | 1939 |

September 24, 1929

American James H. Doolitttle becomes the first aviator to use instrument-guided technology. His take off and landing relying on instrument guidance proves that pilots can be trained to fly through fog, clouds, precipitation, darkness, and other forms of visibility impediments.

May 20, 1932

Amelia Earhart of the United States is the first woman to fly solo across the Atlantic in a Vega aircraft. She travels from Harbour Grace, Newfoundland to arrive in 15 hours at Londonderry, Ireland.

July 14, 1933

Wiley Post, a U.S. pilot, makes the first solo round-the-world flight. Flying around the world in 7 days, Post covers 15,596 miles.

1937

A Turkish aviatrix, Sabiha Gökçen becomes the first female fighter pilot while serving in a military operation against the Dersim rebellion, an uprising against the Turkish government in eastern Turkey.

August 27, 1939

Germany's *Heinkel* He-178, powered by a *Heinkel* S3B turbojet, is the first fully jet-propelled aircraft to fly.

THE GOLDEN AGE

World War II

When Hitler's Blitzkrieg broke across Europe in September 1939, the airplane was in the forefront of the attack and forever changed the way in which wars were fought. No longer could an army control the battlefield or a navy control the sea, without the control of the air overhead. Accelerated by the demands of combat, technology took fantastic leaps forward with the introduction of jets, rockets, radar and navigational aids; all developments that would have pay offs in the future. For aviation, the war brought not just an evolution, but a revolution.

Boeing B-17G *Flying Fortress*

In the years leading up to World War II, many airpower advocates championed the strategic bomber as a means to win wars, or at least intimidate potential enemies. In 1934, the U.S. Army Air Corps was looking for a new strategic bomber and invited manufacturers to compete. The Boeing design was the clear winner, but after a crash destroyed the prototype, it was out of the running. Still, the Army had enough confidence in the design to order 13 YB-17s, and the legend was born.

Sprouting defensive guns from a number of positions, the B-17 was quickly dubbed a *Flying Fortress*, and its long range capability was put to use in many demonstration flights during the 1930s. Only 155 B-17s existed when the Japanese attacked Pearl Harbor, but production quickly accelerated so that by May 1945, more than 12,700 had been built.

Unlike the British who area bombed by night, the United States preferred using the B-17 for daylight precision attacks on enemy strategic industries. Hauling three tons of bombs into the frozen skies, the B-17 *Flying Fortress* served in every theater of war, but was most famous for its Eighth Air Force daylight strategic bombing raids on Germany. Flying in close formation and bristling with machine guns, thousands of B-17s battled through storms of anti-aircraft fire and German fighters to reach their targets, often sustaining incredible amounts of damage, but still bringing their crews home. The B-17 was slower than its counterpart, the B-24 *Liberator*. It carried fewer bombs and could not fly as far, yet because of its sturdy and stout design, its crews trusted their aircraft.

WORLD WAR II

While most B-17s fell to enemy defenses or the scrapper's torch after the war, this one survived to be sold to a civilian operator in 1962. It was used to develop the Fulton "Skyhook," a method to retrieve a man or equipment from the ground without landing, which was demonstrated by this aircraft in the 1964 James Bond movie *Thunderball*. Later, it was acquired by Evergreen for use as an aerial fire bomber, and was eventually returned to its wartime configuration in 1990.

This beautifully restored B-17 *Flying* *Fortress* wears the markings of the Eighth Air Force's 490th Bomb Group, based at Eye, England during World War II.

Specifications

Type:	Bomber
First Flight:	July 28, 1935
Wingspan:	103 feet, 9 inches
Length:	74 feet, 4 inches
Height:	19 feet, 1 inch
Power:	Four Wright R1820-97 Cyclone turbo-supercharged engines
Crew:	10
Top Speed:	287 miles per hour

WORLD WAR II

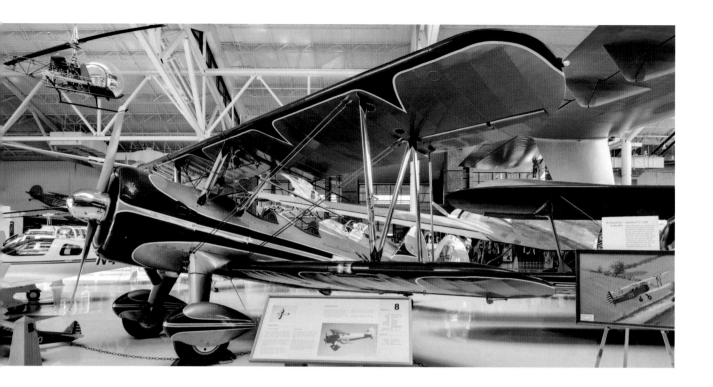

Boeing Stearman Model 75 *Kaydet*

Many World War II aces and flying heroes began their career in a Stearman *Kaydet*. Universally called Stearmans, they were actually built by the Boeing Aircraft Company, which purchased the Stearman Company in 1934. An outdated design in the 1940s, the little biplanes were rugged, maneuverable and ideal for military flight training. Students commonly graduated from primary flight training with 65 hours aloft.

While some Stearmans' paint schemes recapture the colorful U.S. Army or Navy markings of the 1936-1942 period, this *Kaydet* boasts the colorful custom paint scheme of silver and burgundy. It was built in 1943 as a U.S. Navy N2S-5 (the Navy version of the Model E-75, similar to a U.S. Army PT-13D). This crowd-pleasing, air show circuit classic has been modified for special performances, fitted with a 450 horsepower engine and a smoke system. It was formerly owned by astronaut Frank Borman, the commander of the Gemini 7 and Apollo 8 space missions.

Specifications

Type:	Trainer
First Flight:	January 1, 1934
Wingspan:	32 feet, 2 inches
Length:	24 feet
Height:	9 feet, 2 inches
Power:	One Continental R670-5 radial engine
Crew:	2
Top Speed:	150 miles per hour

WORLD WAR II

Curtiss P-40K *Warhawk*

At the outbreak of World War II, Curtiss P-40s formed the backbone of the U.S. Army's fighter corps. With a mid-1930s airframe and engine, the P-40 was said to be outmoded from the start, but it could be built fast and in great numbers. It was the P-40 that struggled into the air to counter Japanese attacks on Pearl Harbor, and it fought with groups from every Allied country, including the American Volunteer Group (*Flying Tigers*) in China and the Tuskegee Airmen.

This P-40 was assigned to the Aleutian Islands in Alaska during World War II. During a mission, most likely in 1944, it suffered an engine malfunction and crash-landed into a fresh water marsh near Port Hayden.

More than 30 years later, the remarkably intact aircraft was airlifted from its resting place via helicopter. It was purchased by Evergreen in 1990 and restored with a *Flying Tigers* paint scheme in honor of Oregon native Ken Jernstedt, a Marine pilot who destroyed a total of 12 enemy aircraft with the American Volunteer Group.

Specifications

Type:	Fighter
First Flight:	October 14, 1938
Wingspan:	37 feet, 3.5 inches
Length:	33 feet, 4 inches
Height:	12 feet, 4 inches
Power:	One Allison V-1710-99 liquid-cooled engine
Crew:	1
Top Speed:	350 miles per hour

WORLD WAR II

Douglas A-26C *Invader*

The Douglas A-26 *Invader* is one of the most versatile combat aircraft ever built, serving in three major wars and a number of minor conflicts in a career that spanned almost three decades.

Designed by legendary engineer Ed Heinemann, the A-26 was capable of fast low-level attack, as well as precision bombing for close support of troops on the ground. Early experience with it in the Pacific was less than encouraging, but modifications were made, and it was reintroduced in Europe during the final months of World War II.

When the Korean War erupted in 1950, the A-26 was first on the scene, operating mostly at night to stop the flow of enemy supplies. Later, *Invaders* were used for counter-insurgency warfare in Vietnam, and the CIA employed many B-26s in Asia, Africa and Latin America.

This A-26 (pictured far left) flew combat with the French Air Force in Indochina before becoming a fire bomber in the 1960s. It was acquired by Evergreen in 1989 and restored over 6,000 hours by Museum volunteers.

Specifications

Type:	Medium Bomber
First Flight:	July 10, 1942
Wingspan:	70 feet
Length:	50 feet
Height:	18 feet, 3 inches
Power:	Two Pratt & Whitney R2800-27 radial engines
Crew:	3
Top Speed:	355 miles per hour

WORLD WAR II

Douglas C-47A *Skytrain*

Officially called *Dakota* in England and *Skytrain* in the United States, soldiers usually referred to C-47s as "Gooney Birds" or just "Goonies." The C-47 is a toughened up version of the successful Douglas DC-3 passenger plane with improved engines, cargo doors big enough to admit a jeep, a strengthened rear fuselage and a beefed-up floor to hold loads of equipment.

They served in every theater of World War II. After the war, during the Berlin Airlift in 1948, "Goonies" helped supply a city from the air with everything from candy to coal. Versions of the C-47 were even modified as gunships during the Vietnam War.

As part of the 89th TCS, the Museum's C-47A took part in the D-Day Invasion of France, June 6, 1944, flying three missions to drop paratroopers and tow gliders. It later participated in Operation Market Garden in Holland, before being returned to the United States, where it eventually served with West Coast Airlines. The Oregon Museum of Science and Industry donated this aircraft to the Museum.

Type:	Cargo
Wingspan:	95 feet, 6 inches
Length:	63 feet, 9 inches
Height:	17 feet
Power:	Two Pratt & Whitney R-1830-90C Twin Wasp radial engines
Crew:	3
Capacity:	28 troops
Top Speed:	224 miles per hour

WORLD WAR II

Fairchild PT-19A

Knowing that thousands of young men would need to learn to fly, the Army asked manufacturers to submit designs for a modern primary training aircraft on the eve of World War II.

In a "fly-off" between 17 companies, the Fairchild Model M-62 was chosen as the new machine to train cadet pilots. Its fabric-covered steel-tube frame construction with plywood covered wings made the PT-19 rugged, reliable and easy to maintain. It was closer to the types of planes that students would fly in combat, yet it had wide landing gear for easy landings and performance that was almost vice-less in flight, earning it the nickname "Cradle of Heroes."

During the war, a shortage of the Ranger engines that powered the PT-19 forced Fairchild to build a radial engine version dubbed the PT-23. In addition, a version with a canopy for cold-weather flying was built for the British Commonwealth Air Training Plan and operated in Canada as the PT-26 *Cornell.*

Specifications

Type:	Trainer
First Flight:	May 15, 1939
Wingspan:	36 feet
Length:	28 feet
Height:	10 feet, 6 inches
Power:	One Fairchild-Ranger L440-3 air-cooled engine
Crew:	2
Top Speed:	132 miles per hour

WORLD WAR II

General Motors TBM-3E *Avenger*

The *Avenger* was the first new aircraft to enter Navy service after the attack on Pearl Harbor, and its name proved fitting. By the end of World War II, *Avenger*s had sunk more than 60 Japanese ships including the world's largest battleship, the *Yamato*. Flying from aircraft carriers in all theaters of war, it excelled as a torpedo bomber but was also used as a dive bomber and for anti-submarine patrol.

As with many *Avenger*s, this Grumman-designed TBM was built by General Motors' Eastern Aircraft Division, and

it flew in VT-37 (Torpedo Squadron 37) and VT-7 early in its career. While with VT-7, it was based at the Naval Air Station in Klamath Falls, Oregon. Afterwards, the airplane served with the Naval Reserve and was struck from Navy records in 1956 with a total of 1,194 hours flown. Purchased by Riverside Aircraft Company two years later, it was converted for aerial spraying and fighting forest fires. It was purchased by Evergreen in 1989, and now wears the paint scheme of the *Avenger*s that flew from the *USS Langley* during World War II.

Specifications

Type:	Torpedo Bomber
First Flight:	August 1, 1941
Wingspan:	54 feet, 2 inches
Length:	40 feet, 11.5 inches
Height:	16 feet, 5 inches
Power:	One Wright R-2600 radial engine
Crew:	3
Top Speed:	251 miles per hour

WORLD WAR II

Goodyear FG-1D *Corsair*

America's fighters were badly out-matched by the nimble Japanese *Zero* at the beginning of World War II, and U.S. pilots paid the price. An aircraft that reversed the trend was the F4U *Corsair.* Fast and heavily armed, it was more than a match for Japanese fighters. Because it was difficult to land on aircraft carriers, it was initially given to the U.S. Marine Corps for land-based operation, although later modifications made it a potent carrier fighter. It was produced in many variants by both Vought and Goodyear, and served in World War II and Korea.

This *Corsair* flew with the Fuerza Area Salvador (the Air Force of El Salvador), and took part in the "Soccer War" between El Salvador and Honduras in 1968. It even seems to have received battle damage, evidenced by a patched bullet hole in its right wing. It was purchased by Evergreen in 1990, and now wears the paint scheme of Navy ace and Oregon native Oscar Chenoweth Jr.'s aircraft. Chenoweth flew with the famed "Jolly Rogers Squadron" (VF-17) and is credited with eight victories.

Specifications

Type:	Fighter
First Flight:	May 29, 1940
Wingspan:	41 feet
Length:	33 feet, 5 inches
Height:	15 feet
Power:	One Pratt & Whitney R-2800 radial engine
Crew:	1
Top Speed:	415 miles per hour

WORLD WAR II

Lockheed P-38L *Lightning*

With four machine guns and a cannon in its nose, the P-38 *Lightning* had enough firepower to sink a ship, and sometimes did. A radical design, it was twice the size and power of any U.S. fighter when it first flew in 1939. German adversaries called it the "Fork-Tailed Devil," and in the Pacific, P-38s were used to ambush Japanese Admiral Yamamoto's plane, killing the architect of the Pearl Harbor attack. America's highest scoring ace, Major Richard Bong, destroyed 40 Japanese planes with a *Lightning*.

Though in flyable condition, the *Lightning* was in need of complete restoration when the Museum acquired it in 1990. Since its "ground up" reconstruction, it is considered one of the finest examples of the classic Lockheed P-38 in the world. This P-38 wears the paint scheme of Lieutenant Colonel Gerald R. Johnson of Eugene, Oregon, who shot down 24 Japanese aircraft.

Specifications

Type:	Fighter
First Flight:	January 27, 1939
Wingspan:	52 feet
Length:	37 feet, 10 inches
Height:	12 feet, 10 inches
Power:	Two Allison V-1710, liquid-cooled engines
Crew:	1
Top Speed:	414 miles per hour

WORLD WAR II

Messerschmitt Bf 109G-10 *Gustav*

When Hitler's Blitzkrieg swept across Europe, the Messerschmitt Bf-109 was the spearhead of the German fighter force; unchallenged until it faced the *Spitfire*. Like Britain's *Spitfire*, the Bf-109 became the symbol of its nation, flying from the war's opening moments to Germany's surrender.

It is estimated that nearly 35,000 Bf-109s were produced and were used in almost every role including fighter, bomber, reconnaissance and attack. While the Bf-109 was deadly in the hands of an expert pilot, it was difficult to fly, and nearly one third of Bf-109s were lost in accidents.

Some of the prime targets for Allied air attacks during World War II were enemy airplane factories and airfields. As a result, much of the documentation regarding aircraft like this Bf-109 was lost. In 1989, Evergreen purchased this Bf-109G-10, which now wears the paint scheme of the world's most prolific fighter ace, Erich Hartmann. He flew into combat more than 800 times and shot down a staggering 352 enemy aircraft during World War II.

Type:	Fighter
First Flight:	May 29, 1935
Wingspan:	32 feet, 6.5 inches
Length:	29 feet, 8 inches
Height:	8 feet, 6 inches
Power:	One Daimler-Benz DB 605 D-1 liquid-cooled engine
Crew:	1
Top Speed:	429 miles per hour

WORLD WAR II

Messerschmitt Me-262A-1 *Schwalbe* Replica

A weapon that could have turned the tide of World War II, the Me-262 changed air warfare forever. Its top speed was nearly 100 miles per hour faster than the best Allied fighters and its armament of four 30mm cannons and 24 unguided rockets was devastating.

Germany flew the world's first jet in August 1939, and the Me-262 *Schwalbe* (Swallow) exploited that technology to become the first jet in combat. Pilots were ecstatic with its performance and Commanding General of Fighters, Adolf Galland, said "it flew as if being pushed

by angels." The Me-262 did have drawbacks, including unreliable engines, short range and poor slow-speed performance. But what contributed most to its demise was a lack of fuel. By the early 1945, Allied bombing had destroyed Germany's ability to produce and transport fuel, leaving many Me-262s grounded.

This reproduction was built by Legend Flyers of Everett, Washington, utilizing the same materials and construction techniques as the original Me-262.

Specifications

Type:	Fighter
First Flight:	July 18, 1942
Wingspan:	41 feet 6 inches
Length:	34 feet 9 inches
Height:	11 feet, 6 inches
Power:	Two Junkers Jumo 004 B-1 turbojet engines
Crew:	1
Top Speed:	559 miles per hour

WORLD WAR II

■ Naval Aircraft Factory N3N-3 *Canary*

The N3N was the only aircraft designed and built by a factory wholly owned by the U.S. Navy. During the 1930s, the Navy needed a more sophisticated trainer. At the same time, it needed to dispose of aluminum angle left over from building the *USS Akron* and *Macon*. The Navy decided to design its own aircraft utilizing the aluminum, solving both problems at once. The N3N first flew in 1935, and the last one retired in 1961.

Like many trainers in World War II, the N3N was nicknamed "Yellow Peril" due to its yellow color scheme and the inexperienced pilot at the controls. Its robust construction helped it survive the beating given to it by student pilots. Purchased by civilian operators, many of them became crop-dusters or aerial sprayers.

The Museum's N3N was restored in the 1970s and purchased by Museum board member Ernest McCall in 1975. McCall donated it in 2008.

Type:	Trainer
First Flight:	August 1935
Wingspan:	32 feet, 8 inches
Length:	25 feet, 6 inches
Height:	10 feet, 10 inches
Power:	One Wright R760-2 Whirlwind radial engine
Crew:	2
Top Speed:	126 miles per hour

WORLD WAR II

North American P-51D *Mustang*

Able to fly long distances and escort heavy bombers at a high altitude, the P-51 was equal to or better than almost every enemy fighter it encountered. Fast from the start, the *Mustang* went from the drawing board to a physical aircraft in just 117 days. It was originally powered with an Allison engine, but real success came with the Packard Merlin engine. It added speed, power and maneuverability to the *Mustang*, making it one of the greatest piston engine fighters ever created. *Mustang*s operated in Europe and the Pacific, as well as in the Korean War. When asked about

the *Mustang*, one pilot stated, "It was elegantly simple and simply elegant."

Used primarily as a racer in national speed races, this *Mustang* passed through various owners until 1977, when it was discovered that it had less than 400 hours of flying time. The *Mustang* was then fully restored, a project that took nearly ten years. Evergreen acquired the plane in 1986, and it quickly became a favorite of Museum co-founder, Michael King Smith.

Specifications

Type:	Fighter
First Flight:	October 26, 1940
Wingspan:	37 feet
Length:	32 feet, 3 inches
Height:	13 feet, 8 inches
Power:	One Rolls-Royce Merlin 724-1C liquid-cooled engine
Crew:	1
Top Speed:	437 miles per hour

WORLD WAR II

North American SNJ-4 (T-6) *Texan*

Called "the most universally used airplane in history," the *Texan* rivals the famed DC-3 in longevity and variety of uses. Employed as an advanced trainer in World War II, the *Texan* was designated T-6 by the U.S. Army and the SNJ by the Navy.

After student pilots graduated from slow primary trainers, they used *Texan*s to master flight in more complex aircraft before entering combat in high performance planes like *Mustang*s and *Corsair*s. After the war, the *Texan*s continued in U.S. service and flew with at least 55 nations in the role of trainer, fighter, bomber, attack, transport and observation aircraft.

Assigned serial number 88-13466 and Navy bureau number 27780, this SNJ-4 was accepted into the Navy in 1943 and served until 1956. During the mid-1960s, the airframe was reportedly altered for weather modification flights, but was later restored to its original configuration. The SNJ-4 passed through numerous owners before coming to Evergreen in March 1986.

Specifications

Type:	Trainer
First Flight:	April 1, 1935
Wingspan:	42 feet
Length:	29 feet
Height:	11 feet, 9 inches
Power:	One Pratt & Whitney R-1340 radial engine
Crew:	2
Top Speed:	205 miles per hour

WORLD WAR II

Piper L-4H *Grasshopper*

Although the Piper J-3 *Cub* was originally designed as a civilian aircraft, it was drafted into military service during World War II for battlefield reconnaissance, liaison duties and casualty evacuation.

Renamed the Piper L-4H *Grasshopper*, military leaders like General Eisenhower and General Patton also used the L-4s to fly around the battlefields and maintain contact with their commanders. Some *Grasshopper* pilots, however, were not content to just observe the war and instead chose to be active participants.

For instance, Major Charles Carpenter mounted bazooka anti-tank rocket weapons on the wing struts of his L-4 and destroyed German armored vehicles in France after D-Day; earning him the nickname "Bazooka Charlie." The L-4 is also known for emerging victorious against a German Fiesler *Storch* in the last dogfight of World War II in Europe.

This L-4H was meticulously restored by the Museum's restoration director, Colin Powers, and has won numerous awards for quality and fidelity. It was acquired in 2007.

Specifications

Type:	Observation / Liaison
First Flight:	August 1935
Wingspan:	35 feet, 3 inches
Length:	22 feet, 5 inches
Height:	6 feet, 8 inches
Power:	One Continental A-65-8 air-cooled engine
Crew:	2
Top Speed:	87 miles per hour

■ **Ryan** PT-22 *Recruit*

Specifications

As World War II approached, the U.S. Army Air Corps realized it would eventually be drawn into the conflict and need more pilots. It also needed more advanced training aircraft to prepare those pilots to fly. Prior to 1940, the Army only purchased biplanes for training, but because of advances in combat aircraft, they now needed higher performance monoplanes.

A variant of the Ryan ST series sport planes, the PT-22 and its predecessor, the PT-16, were the first monoplane trainers to be acquired. Because the

Menasco engines used on the PT-16s were not particularly reliable, the *Recruit* was introduced in 1941 with a powerful Kinner radial engine. More than 1,000 served with the U.S. military. The PT-22 was more challenging to fly than other primary trainers of the time and was ideal for students who would take high performance fighters and bombers into combat in World War II.

This PT-22 *Recruit* was acquired in 2008.

Type:	Trainer
First Flight:	June 8, 1934
Wingspan:	30 feet, 1 inch
Length:	22 feet, 7 inches
Height:	7 feet, 2 inches
Power:	One Kinner R540-1 radial engine
Crew:	2
Top Speed:	125 miles per hour

WORLD WAR II

Supermarine *Spitfire* Mk. XVI

Few aircraft are considered legends, but the *Spitfire* is truly one of them. Its streamlined form and distinctive elliptical wing reveal a resemblance to the Supermarine racing planes of the 1920s and 30s.

Entering service in 1939, the *Spitfire* became a symbol of England's finest hour when the Royal Air Force, equipped with "the Spit" and the Hawker *Hurricane*, defeated Hitler's bombers in the Battle of Britain. The *Spitfire* evolved throughout World War II, with each successive model bettering the breed. The *Spitfire* Mark XVI was one of the later variants of the classic fighter with cannon armament and a "bubble" canopy.

After appearing in the 1969 movie *Battle of Britain*, this aircraft went to the Number 4 Squadron of the Central Flying School. Acquired by the Warbirds of Great Britain, the plane was completely restored, and then purchased by Evergreen in 1990.

Specifications

Type:	Fighter
First Flight:	March 5, 1936
Wingspan:	36 feet, 10 inches
Length:	31 feet, 5 inches
Height:	11 feet, 6 inches
Power:	One Rolls-Royce Merlin liquid-cooled engine
Crew:	1
Top Speed:	404 miles per hour

WORLD WAR II

Hughes HK-1 (H-4) Flying Boat *Spruce Goose*

As the largest airplane ever constructed and flown only one time, the Hughes Flying Boat represents one of man's greatest attempts to conquer the skies. It was born out of a need to move troops and material across the Atlantic Ocean, where in 1942, German submarines were sinking hundreds of Allied ships. Henry Kaiser, steel magnate and shipbuilder, conceived the idea of the massive flying transport, and turned to Howard Hughes to design and build it. Hughes took on the task, along with the government mandate not to use materials critical to the war effort such as steel and aluminum. Six times bigger than any aircraft of its time, the Flying Boat is made out of wood!

Completed after the end of World War II, the winged giant made only one flight on November 2, 1947. The unannounced decision to fly was made by Hughes during a taxi test. The flight went only a little more than a mile at an altitude of 70 feet for about one minute. But, the short hop proved to skeptics that the gigantic machine could fly!

Originally designated HK-1 for the first aircraft built by Hughes-Kaiser, the giant was re-designated H-4 when Henry Kaiser withdrew from the project in 1944. The press insisted on calling the Hughes Flying Boat the "Spruce Goose;" a name that Hughes despised. Ironically, most of the huge plane is actually made of birch.

The H-4 went into storage after its famous flight and was kept out of the public eye for 33 years. All that time, Hughes kept the plane ready to fly. After his death in 1976, it was purchased by entrepreneur Jack Wrather, who

Above: Howard Hughes and flight engineer at the engineer station, November 2, 1947.

Top Right: Hughes Flying Boat, circa 1947.

Bottom Right: The famous flight of the Hughes Flying Boat, November 2, 1947.

moved it into a domed hangar in Long Beach, California. In 1988, the Wrather Corporation was bought by The Walt Disney Company, which did not see the plane in its future plans. Evergreen Aviation & Space Museum co-founders, Michael King Smith and Delford M. Smith, submitted the winning proposal in 1992 to provide the aviation icon with a proper home.

Beginning that year, the Flying Boat was disassembled and transported by barge up the West Coast, then down the Columbia and Willamette Rivers,

to Portland, Oregon. It remained there for several months, until water levels permitted the huge structures to safely pass under the Willamette's many bridges. Finally, in February 1993, the aircraft was transported by truck for the last 7.5 miles to McMinnville, Oregon. Temporary hangars were built as housing for the aircraft, while volunteers worked on the aircraft's restoration. In 2001, assembly of the Hughes Flying Boat was completed in its new home.

Specifications

Type:	Cargo Aircraft Prototype
First Flight:	November 2, 1947
Wingspan:	319 feet, 11 inches
Length:	218 feet, 8 inches
Height:	79 feet, 4 inches
Power:	Eight Pratt & Whitney R-4360, radial engines
Crew:	18
Capacity:	750 troops or two Sherman tanks
Top Speed:	227-231 miles per hour

WORLD WAR II

AVIATION TIMELINE

1940   **1940**   **1941**   **1942**   **1943**

February 15, 1940

The Air Transport Auxiliary (ATA), a British civilian pilot organization that includes both men and women, begins ferrying new, repaired and damaged military aircraft, as well as transport of mail and medical supplies.

July 10, 1940

The German Air Force, or *Luftwaffe*, begins its air campaign to destroy Britain's Royal Air Force (RAF) in the Battle of Britain. The Battle is the first major campaign to be fought entirely by air forces. It is also the largest and most sustained aerial bombing campaign of that time.

December 1, 1941

The Civil Air Patrol, the civilian auxiliary of the United States Air Force, is established. Serving as coastal patrols, civilian pilots surprise enemy submarines with feigning dive-bomb attacks, forcing subs to head for deeper water. A Nazi submariner later admits that the U-boats were pulled back "because of those damned little red and yellow airplanes" flown by the Civil Air Patrol.

June 4, 1942

Japan arrives in Midway to defeat the U.S. in a surprise attack. But the Battle of Midway will mark a major reversal in the tide of the war as the Americans surprise the Japanese with a vigorous attack starting with a wave of Douglas TBD *Devastator* torpedo planes. With their fleet unprotected, Japan soon faces a follow-up attack by Douglas SBD *Dauntless*es. Japan will lose 4 aircraft carriers and 250 planes.

May 30, 1943

The Tuskegee Airmen, the first African American military aviators, engage in their first air assault on the island of Pantelleria, Italy. Overcome by air power, the island population will surrender. The Airmen will eventually be credited with many other accomplishments such as a good record in protecting U.S. bombers, only losing 25 out of hundreds of missions.

WORLD WAR II

1943   1943   1944   1945   1945

August 5, 1943

The Women Airforce Service Pilots (WASP) is created through the merger of the Women's Flying Training Detachment (WFTD) and the Women's Auxiliary Ferrying Squadron (WAFS). Through WASP, U.S. female pilots take on missions such as ferrying aircraft from factories to military bases, originally controlled by male pilots now serving in the war.

September 1, 1943

The Grumman F6F *Hellcat* sees first action. It is specifically designed to defeat the Japanese *Zero* and soon gains a reputation for outstanding performance and craftsmanship. With the *Hellcat*, Naval aviators rack up an impressive record: 4,947 out of 6,477 aerial victories in the Pacific theater.

March 1944

The North American Aviation P-51 *Mustang* debuts as the first fighter capable of escorting bombers all the way to Germany. It soon gains the reputation of being one of the best, if not the best, fighters of the war. *Mustang* pilots will claim 4,950 enemy aircraft shot down, the most of any Allied fighter in conflict.

March 1945

One fourth of the German war economy is neutralized because of damage from repeated strategic bombing strikes. With its oil supply destroyed, transportation systems cracking, and most of Germany's factories and telephones no longer working; troops and equipment cannot mobilize.

May 8, 1945

The German fighter pilot Erich Hartmann makes his last kill. Hartmann is the highest-scoring fighter ace in the history of aerial warfare. He will claim 352 aerial victories in 1,404 combat missions and will engage in 825 aerial combats with the *Luftwaffe*. Hartmann is never shot down or forced to land due to fire from enemy aircraft.

WORLD WAR II

Korea and Vietnam Era

The end of World War II brought major changes in aviation. Utilizing the technologies designed to win the war, aircraft could now travel faster, farther, higher and safer. Airlines expanded rapidly using the new transport planes developed in World War II, and air travel became possible not just for the rich and famous, but for everybody. And with the advent of the jet airliner, the speed of travel shrank the globe and helped to open a worldwide economy. Life on Earth would never be the same.

Lockheed SR-71A *Blackbird*

In the world of aviation, there is no production aircraft that flies higher or faster than the SR-71 *Blackbird*. Born out of a Cold War need to keep tabs on America's adversaries, this unarmed reconnaissance aircraft was unequaled in performance, setting an altitude record at 85,069 feet and a speed record at 2,193 mph; both on the same day!

Even as Kelly Johnson and the team at Lockheed's "Skunk Works" were designing the high flying U-2 reconnaissance plane, they knew the only safety a sky spy had was to go faster and higher. With that in mind they developed the A-12 for the CIA, which utilized a "double-delta" wing design and a pair of unique engines that acted as turbojets at low speed and ramjets at high speed. Modified to meet the U.S. Air Force's requirements, the design evolved into the SR-71A.

Building an aircraft that would operate at high speeds at the edge of the atmosphere required some incredible feats of engineering. To deal with the extreme temperatures generated at such high speeds, the aircraft structure and skin were made mostly of titanium, much of which had to be obtained from the Soviet Union through "front" companies. To deal with the high speed, the engines had to be designed with a movable spike in the inlet that adjusted the airflow and kept the air entering the engine at sub-sonic speeds. And, at high altitudes, the stresses on the pilots were such that they had to wear pressure suits similar to those worn later by space shuttle astronauts.

Entering service with the Air Force in 1966, *Blackbird*s were based at

KOREA AND VIETNAM ERA

Beale AFB California. Detachments at Mildenhall, England and Kadena, Okinawa, made SR-71s available at short notice for work in any of the world's trouble spots. *Blackbirds* operated all along the borders of the Soviet Union and China, and regularly took part in operations to photograph targets in the Middle East, Vietnam, North Korea and Cuba. Often fired upon with anti-aircraft missiles, the SR-71 would simply accelerate away from them, and no *Blackbird* was ever shot down, although 12 were lost in accidents.

Its high cost and the proliferation of reconnaissance satellites brought an end to the SR-71 operations in 1989, but world tensions brought them out of retirement in 1993 for a five year period. NASA used three SR-71s for high speed research, but they too were retired by 1999, ending the career of this record-setting aircraft.

The Museum's SR-71A *Blackbird*, which was one of the three flown by NASA, and much of its support equipment is on loan from the National Museum of the United States Air Force.

Specifications

Type:	Reconnaissance
First Flight:	April 30, 1962
Wingspan:	55 feet, 7 inches
Length:	107 feet, 5 inches
Height:	18 feet, 6 inches
Power:	Two Pratt & Whitney J-58 afterburning turbojets
Crew:	2
Top Speed:	2,200+ miles per hour (Mach 3.2+)

KOREA AND VIETNAM ERA

Beechcraft *Bonanza 35*

It seems this airplane was destined to be a success from the start. Beechcraft chose the name *Bonanza*, which means "a rich source of profit or gain, or an unusual value." The revolutionary private plane could be considered both.

Developed after World War II, the *Bonanza* was loaded with modern features including retractable tricycle landing gear, controllable pitch propeller and instruments for foul weather flying. Its most recognizable feature is the unique "V" tail where the control surfaces work as both rudders and elevators, lowering drag and making the aircraft faster and more fuel-efficient.

This particular *Bonanza*, referred to as a "Straight 35," was one of the first developed in 1947. After years of flying for a pet supply company, the aircraft was acquired by Joe Koller, Jr., and converted back to its original flying condition. Koller then donated his prized aircraft to the Museum in 2000.

Specifications	
Type:	General Aviation
First Flight:	December 22, 1945
Wingspan:	32 feet, 10 inches
Length:	25 feet, 2 inches
Height:	6 feet, 6.5 inches
Power:	One Continental E185-1 air-cooled engine
Crew:	1
Capacity:	3
Top Speed:	184 miles per hour

Beechcraft T-34B *Mentor*

Following World War II the military shrank dramatically, but despite the force reduction, pilots still needed training. Walter Beech felt he could produce a trainer that would be far more economical to operate than former World War II trainers, based on the Model 35 *Bonanza* sport aircraft.

Utilizing the *Bonanza*'s wings, tail and engine, a slimmer, two-seat tandem fuselage replaced the sport aircraft cabin in this private venture. After years of aggressive marketing, Beech convinced the Air Force to buy the T-34 in 1952.

The Navy was also searching for a new primary trainer and selected the T-34, but not without changes. These included a non-steerable nose wheel, changes in wing dihedral, and springs to increase elevator force, all of which made the aircraft more stable. The Navy would use the T-34B for over 20 years, taking students from their first flight, on through their solo, aerobatic training and formation flying.

This *Mentor* is on loan from the National Museum of Naval Aviation.

Specifications

Type:	Trainer
First Flight:	December 2, 1948
Wingspan:	32 feet, 8 inches
Length:	29 feet, 9 inches
Height:	9 feet, 6 inches
Power:	One Continental E-185 air-cooled engine
Crew:	2
Top Speed:	178 miles per hour

KOREA AND VIETNAM ERA

■ **Convair** F-102A *Delta Dagger*

Specifications

Designed when supersonic flight was relatively new, the delta-wing F-102 was beset with troubles from the start. Built as an interceptor, the aircraft could not be coaxed over the sound barrier. A radical redesign included a more powerful engine, a streamlined nose and an "area rule" where the fuselage becomes thinner in the middle, like the shape of a soda bottle. By reducing the cross section where the wings joined, drag was greatly reduced to produce a winning design. This concept is still used on high-performance aircraft today.

In February 1963, this F-102 was transferred to the 337th Fighter Group based at Portland International Airport, and nearly three years later, the plane flew with the 142nd Fighter Group of the Air National Guard. In 1971, the plane was retired and transferred into the Air Force's museum loan program.

In 1998, the F-102 was brought to the Museum from the Oregon Museum of Science and Industry. Today, the canopy rails carry the names of Major Bill Avolio and Brigadier General Patrick O'Grady.

Type:	Fighter
First Flight:	October 24, 1953
Wingspan:	38 feet, 1.5 inches
Length:	68 feet, 3 inches
Height:	21 feet, 2.5 inches
Power:	One Pratt & Whitney J57-P-35 engine
Crew:	1
Top Speed:	858 miles per hour (Mach 1.25)

KOREA AND VIETNAM ERA

■ **Convair** F-106A *Delta Dart*

Specifications

During the Cold War, the U.S. Air Force was on guard against any threat and employed high-performance, missile-armed interceptors around U.S. borders. While the F-102 *Delta Dagger* had served admirably in this role, the late 1950s saw an effort by Convair to squeeze more performance out of the design. The result was a whole new aircraft; the F-106 *Delta Dart*. The F-106 featured a more powerful radar, a higher performance engine and new air intakes to deal with the Mach 2+ speeds that it would fly.

The F-106A was armed with up to six air-to-air missiles, including the radar-guided *Falcon* missile and the unguided *Genie* nuclear missile. The latter was designed to detonate in the midst of a bomber formation, bringing down several enemy aircraft in one atomic blast. Luckily, the F-106 was never called upon to fire a shot in anger.

The *Delta Dart* was restored at the Evergreen Maintenance Center and carries the markings of its final operating squadron, the 49th FIS at Griffiss Air Force Base.

Type:	Interceptor
First Flight:	December 26, 1956
Wingspan:	38 feet, 3 inches
Length:	70 feet, 7 inches
Height:	20 feet, 4 inches
Power:	One Pratt & Whitney J-75 afterburning turbojet
Crew:	1
Top Speed:	1,525 miles per hour (Mach 2.3)

KOREA AND VIETNAM ERA

de Havilland D.H. 100 *Vampire* FB.9

The second British single-engine jet fighter in service with the Royal Air Force, the *Vampire* was designed and built during World War II, flying only weeks before the war in Europe ended. Designed in the early days of jets, the short, stubby center fuselage minimized the complicated ductwork for the engine's air intake and exhaust. This led to an aircraft with twin tail booms, and the engine directly behind the pilot. With no propeller, the *Vampire* has shorter landing gear and sits low to the ground. In order to save weight, the cockpit section was built from sandwiched balsa and plywood.

"Mark 9s" were developed after pilots in earlier models suffered heat exhaustion while stationed in hot climates. The Museum's aircraft was built with a Godfrey refrigerator unit incorporated into the starboard wing intake fillet to provide air conditioning. The earliest known operator of the Museum's *Vampire* was the Government of India. In 1986, the *Vampire* was purchased by Don Fitzgerald and donated to the Museum in 1999.

Specifications

Type:	Fighter
First Flight:	April 20, 1945
Wingspan:	38 feet
Length:	30 feet, 9 inches
Height:	6 feet, 10 inches
Power:	One de Havilland Goblin 3 turbojet
Crew:	1
Top Speed:	548 miles per hour

KOREA AND VIETNAM ERA

Douglas AD-5N *Skyraider*

Designed as a high-performance dive/ torpedo bomber, the Douglas AD *Skyraider* series of aircraft was too late to see service in World War II, but served with distinction in both the Korean and Vietnam Wars. Able to carry a bomb load equal to that of a four-engined B-17 *Flying Fortress*, the AD (re-designated A-1 in the 1960s) specialized in close-in support of troops on the ground. Despite being a bit of an anachronism in the jet age, the *Skyraider* proved invaluable during search and rescue operations, as its lower speed and longer endurance meant it could

circle over a downed airman or escort helicopters where a jet could not.

The AD-5 (A-1E) variant of the *Skyraider* carried a crew of four in its widened fuselage, and the AD-5N was specialized for night attack and electronics warfare.

This *Skyraider* was acquired by Evergreen in 2005 after spending many years in the yard of a Pennsylvania boys' school. It has been restored through the efforts of the Museum's restoration volunteers.

Type:	Attack Bomber / Electronic Warfare
First Flight:	March 18, 1945
Wingspan:	50 feet
Length:	38 feet, 10 inches
Height:	15 feet, 8 inches
Power:	One Wright R3350-26WA radial engine
Crew:	4
Top Speed:	322 miles per hour

KOREA AND VIETNAM ERA

Douglas A-4E *Skyhawk*

Early in the Korean War, designer Ed Heinemann became concerned with the growing weight and cost of fighters and set out to design one to reverse the trend. The result was the A-4 *Skyhawk*, one of the lightest attack aircraft ever built. The smallest aircraft ever capable of carrying a nuclear weapon, it won fame hauling conventional bombs in Vietnam, bearing the brunt of the Navy's missions in the first years of the war. One even shot down a MiG-17 using an unguided rocket. Later, the *Skyhawk* went into combat again with the Argentines in the 1982 Falklands

War and with the Kuwaiti Air Force during Operation Desert Storm. Versions were also used as trainers, and the *Skyhawk* was a brilliant performer with the U.S. Navy's *Blue Angels* for 13 years.

This A-4E has the markings of Lieutenant Commander John S. McCain III aboard the *USS Forrestal* in 1967, when his aircraft was struck by a missile accidentally launched off another aircraft. The resulting fire destroyed 21 aircraft and claimed 134 lives.

Specifications

Type:	Attack Bomber
First Flight:	June 22, 1954
Wingspan:	26 feet, 6 inches
Length:	40 feet, 3 inches
Height:	15 feet
Power:	One Pratt & Whitney J52-P-6A turbojet engine
Crew:	1
Top Speed:	673 miles per hour

KOREA AND VIETNAM ERA

■ **Grumman** OV-1D *Mohawk*

In its role as an observation and electronic reconnaissance airplane, the OV-1 *Mohawk* excelled at supplying Army field commanders with information about enemy forces in daylight, darkness or bad weather.

Loaded with electronics and cameras, *Mohawk*s saw extensive service during the Vietnam War. They also served in Europe, Korea, Central and South America, Southeast Asia and Alaska, as well as in Operation Desert Storm. The Oregon National Guard's OV-1s worked with local law enforcement agencies, the

U.S. Border Patrol, U.S. Coast Guard, U.S. Customs and U.S. Navy for drug interdiction, firefighting and pollution patrol in the Columbia River.

Delivered into military service in 1968, this *Mohawk* flew until November 1991. This D-model, serial number 67-18902, was actually converted from a C-model. The aircraft is on loan from the Oregon Military Museum through the auspices of the U.S. Army and the Oregon Military Department.

Specifications

Type:	Observation / Reconnaissance
First Flight:	April 14, 1959
Wingspan:	48 feet
Length:	41 feet
Height:	13 feet
Power:	Two Avco Lycoming T53-L-701 turboprop engines
Crew:	2
Top Speed:	305 miles per hour

KOREA AND VIETNAM ERA

Grumman TF-9J *Cougar*

During the Korean War, the Grumman F9F *Panther* was the Navy's workhorse fighter, but it was out-classed by the Soviet MiG-15. In response, Grumman created the F9F-6 *Cougar*. Since the *Panther* was such a robust aircraft, Grumman retained the basic layout, sweeping the wings, adding an "all flying" stabilizer and upgrading the engine for higher performance.

Because aircraft carrier flying is a demanding task, the Navy needed a high performance trainer to introduce student pilots to carrier operations.

With the addition of a second seat, the *Cougar* proved to be ideal. The Navy acquired 377 two-seat F9F-8Ts, changed to TF-9J in 1962, to use in training. The only *Cougar*s to see combat were a group of TF-9Js that flew as Forward Air Control aircraft in Vietnam with the Marine Corps.

This aircraft is on loan from the National Museum of Naval Aviation, and is painted as the narrator's aircraft for the U.S. Navy's *Blue Angels* flight demonstration team.

Specifications

Type:	Fighter / Trainer
First Flight:	September 20, 1951
Wingspan:	34 feet, 6 inches
Length:	42 feet, 2 inches
Height:	12 feet, 2 inches
Power:	One Pratt & Whitney J48-P-8A turbojet
Crew:	2
Top Speed:	647 miles per hour

KOREA AND VIETNAM ERA

Lockheed GTD-21B Drone

Specifications

Type:	Reconnaissance
First Flight:	December 22, 1964
Wingspan:	19 feet, 3 inches
Length:	42 feet, 10 inches
Height:	6 feet
Power:	One Marquardt RJ43-MA-11 ramjet
Crew:	Unmanned
Top Speed:	2,700 miles per hour (Mach 3.3+)

Following the shoot-down of Francis Gary Powers and his U-2 in May 1960, it became clear to the intelligence community that there were some places too dangerous to send a manned aircraft. Thus, Lockheed chose to design an unmanned reconnaissance drone. Utilizing a ram jet engine, the D-21 carried cameras in a module that was ejected at the end of the mission and captured in mid-air. The D-21 itself would self-destruct.

Beginning in 1964, D-21s were launched from the back of an A-12 in flight, but on the fourth attempt, the drone collided with the *Blackbird* and resulted in the loss of both vehicles and one life. After that, they were launched from B-52 bombers. Of the 21 drones launched, only seven were successful. Four were launched operationally to spy on the Chinese nuclear test facility at Lop Nor, but all were failures and the program was cancelled in 1971.

The Museum's example, a GTD-21B, is on loan from the National Museum of the U.S. Air Force.

KOREA AND VIETNAM ERA

Lockheed F-104G *Starfighter*

Called the "Missile With A Man In It," the Lockheed F-104 *Starfighter* was one of the most radical and innovative designs of its time; created by Kelly Johnson of Lockheed's "Skunk Works" after conversations with U.S. fighter pilots in the Korean War. It was light-weight with lots of thrust, which gave the F-104 blistering acceleration and its razor-sharp wing was optimized for supersonic flight.

Placed in service as an interceptor to counter Soviet bombers, the *Starfighter* had a relatively short service life with the U.S. Air Force. Needing multi-role fighters more than interceptors, the F-104 dropped from favor with the Pentagon, but ended up finding its biggest customers in foreign sales. Acquired by numerous NATO nations, it was built under license in Germany, Canada, Italy and Japan and used as a fighter/ground attack aircraft.

This F-104G *Starfighter* was built for the Belgian Air Force and was sold to a civilian operator after being declared surplus. Acquired by Evergreen in 2009, it was restored by Museum volunteers.

Specifications

Type:	Interceptor
First Flight:	March 4, 1954
Wingspan:	21 feet, 9 inches
Length:	54 feet, 8 inches
Height:	13 feet, 6 inches
Power:	One General Electric J79-GE-11A afterburning turbojet
Crew:	1
Top Speed:	1,328 miles per hour

KOREA AND VIETNAM ERA

Lockheed P2V-5 *Neptune*

Early in World War II, German U-boats took a heavy toll on Allied ships, which was stemmed by the presence of patrolling aircraft. Lockheed developed its P2V *Neptune* to combat this menace, but due to priority delays, it did not fly until after the war.

The *Neptune* was the last radial-engined bomber to serve in the U.S., and one of the first to fly with both piston and jet engines. A P2V nicknamed "the Truculent Turtle" set a record in 1946 for the longest un-refueled flight, 11,237 miles—a record unbroken until 1962. Setting the norm for modern patrol planes, the *Neptune* was transformed from an armed patrol bomber to dedicated submarine hunter equipped with anti-submarine electronics to keep Soviet subs in check throughout the Cold War.

After retirement, the *Neptune* found a market with civilian operators as a fire bomber. Carrying 2,400 gallons of retardant in a belly tank, the Museum's P2V-5 worked as an aerial firefighter for Evergreen International Aviation.

Type:	Patrol Bomber
First Flight:	May 17, 1945
Wingspan:	100 feet
Length:	77 feet, 10 inches
Height:	28 feet, 4 inches
Power:	Two Pratt & Whitney R3350-32W turbo-compound radial engines, Two Westinghouse J34-WE-22 turbojet engines
Crew:	9-11
Top Speed:	278 miles per hour

KOREA AND VIETNAM ERA

■ **Lockheed** T-33A *Shooting Star*

The U.S. Air Force joined the Jet Age in 1944 with the P-80 *Shooting Star*, its first operational fighter jet. Shortly thereafter, the need arose for a trainer to acquaint pilots with the performance of jets. Lockheed modified the P-80 to add a second seat to produce a trainer. Dubbed the "T-Bird," the T-33A proved to be a graceful and reliable flyer that made the transition to jets easy. For more than 40 years, the T-33A operated with the U.S. Air Force, Navy, Marines and more than 40 other countries.

This aircraft is on loan from the

National Museum of the United States Air Force. Today, the plane's canopy rail carries the name of Major General Charles A. Sams, former commander of the Oregon Air National Guard. When Sams joined the Air Guard in 1955, he flew his first sortie in this almost brand new T-33. In 1985, Sams flew this aircraft again on his "champagne flight," his last mission before retirement.

Specifications

Type:	Trainer
First Flight:	March 22, 1948
Wingspan:	38 feet, 11 inches (without tip tanks)
Length:	37 feet, 9 inches
Height:	11 feet, 8 inches
Power:	One Allison J33 turbojet
Crew:	2
Top Speed:	600 miles per hour

KOREA AND VIETNAM ERA

McDonnell KDD-1 *Katydid* Drone

Specifications

Prior to 1941, the battleship was considered master of the seas, and the only thing that it had to fear was other battleships. But as Pearl Harbor and the sinking of the *HMS Prince of Wales* and *HMS Repulse* showed, the battleship's principle enemy was now the airplane. Throughout the war, ships of all nations were upgraded with more anti-aircraft guns requiring more trained gunners.

To make gunnery training realistic, the U.S. Navy selected McDonnell Aircraft to design and build a high speed, unmanned target drone to simulate fast moving aircraft. The result was the *Katydid*. Powered by a pulse jet similar to the German V-1 *Buzz Bomb*, the KDD-1 could be launched from a ground based catapult or from the wing of a PB4Y *Privateer* bomber. It was steered by commands of a radio operator and at the end of its flight, would be brought back to Earth by parachute for re-use.

This *Katydid* was a gift of the National Air & Space Museum and was restored by Evergreen volunteers in 2009.

Type:	Target
Wingspan:	12 feet, 6 inches
Length:	11 feet, 2 inches
Power:	One McDonnell 7" Pulse jet
Crew:	Unmanned
Top Speed:	175 miles per hour

KOREA AND VIETNAM ERA

McDonnell Douglas F-4C *Phantom II*

Specifications

The McDonnell Douglas F-4 *Phantom II* is one of the most successful fighters to enter service since World War II; an aircraft that could seemingly do everything well. Designed as a carrier-based fighter for the U.S. Navy, it was adopted by the Air Force for fighter/bomber duties, as well as a photo reconnaissance platform. It was the dominant U.S. warplane in the Vietnam War, dropping countless tons of bombs and destroying 151 enemy aircraft in air-to-air combat, but at a cost of 678 losses. *Phantom*s have equipped the air forces of 12 countries, with the final one being built in 1981. Due to its flexibility and versatility, a number of F-4 *Phantom*s are still flying with foreign air forces today, 50+ years after the first flight.

This aircraft last flew with the Oregon Air National Guard's 123rd Fighter Squadron at Portland IAP and carries two "kill markings" denoting victories scored using this aircraft in Vietnam. It is on loan from the National Museum of the United States Air Force.

Type:	Fighter / Interceptor / Bomber / Reconnaissance
First Flight:	May 27, 1958
Wingspan:	38 feet, 5 inches
Length:	63 feet
Height:	16 feet, 6 inches
Power:	Two Pratt & Whitney J79-GE-17A afterburning turbojets
Crew:	2
Top Speed:	1,472 miles per hour

KOREA AND VIETNAM ERA

Mikoyan-Gurevich MiG-15UTI *Midget*

Becoming one of the most feared aircraft ever is not an easy task, but the Soviet Union's Mikoyan MiG-15 did just that. Its arrival over Korea in 1950 was a surprise to Allied pilots who learned to fear this agile fighter with a powerful punch. Designed around a British engine and captured German engineering data, the Soviets made great leaps forward in technology with the MiG-15. Over 12,000 were made for the Soviet Union and its allies.

This MiG-15 UTI was built in China by the Shenyang Aircraft Factory, which repaired 534 battle-damaged, Soviet-built MiG-15s during the Korean War and began constructing their own two-seat MiG-15 UTIs. Versions of the plane were exported to Albania, Bangladesh, North Korea, North Vietnam, Pakistan and Tanzania under the designation FT-2.

Little is known about this aircraft's flight record before it was obtained by Aviation Classics Limited in the late 1980s. Sold to Evergreen in 1992, this airplane is a rare example of one of the first Soviet jet fighters.

Specifications

Type:	Trainer
First Flight:	December 30, 1947
Wingspan:	33 feet
Length:	36.4 feet
Height:	12.1 feet
Power:	One Klimov VK-1 turbojet
Crew:	2
Top Speed:	668 miles per hour

KOREA AND VIETNAM ERA

Mikoyan-Gurevich MiG-17A *Fresco*

An outgrowth of the innovative MiG-15, the nimble, lightweight MiG-17 was a worthy adversary to heavier American aircraft in the skies over Vietnam. When Western observers first saw the MiG-17, they assumed it was simply a lengthened MiG-15; but it was in fact a very different airplane. Because of aerodynamic improvements, the MiG-17 flew higher, farther, faster and was much more stable. Its heavy cannon armament made it a formidable fighter and more than 30 countries utilized the MiG-17. During the Vietnam War, the MiG-17 became a potent killer, shooting down more than 70 U.S. aircraft in combat, while others saw action with the air forces of Egypt, Syria, Sri Lanka, Nigeria and North Korea. The name *Fresco* comes from the NATO codename applied to the type; with the "F" denoting a fighter and two syllables denoting a jet.

Originally built in the Soviet Union, George Gould of Galveston, Texas, purchased this MiG-17A from the Bulgarian Air Force and donated it to the Museum in 2003.

Specifications

Type:	Fighter / Interceptor
First Flight:	January 14, 1950
Wingspan:	31 feet, 7 inches
Length:	37 feet, 3 inches
Height:	12 feet, 6 inches
Power:	One Klimov VK-1F afterburning turbojet
Crew:	1
Top Speed:	711 miles per hour

Mikoyan-Gurevich MiG-21MF *Fishbed-J*

During the Cold War, as the U.S. and U.S.S.R. built bombers to strike each other's cities, they also developed interceptors to protect those cities. The U.S. developed aircraft like the F-104 or F-106, while the Soviets relied on the MiG-21.

Created by the Mikoyan-Gurevich Design Bureau, the MiG-21 would be in production longer than any other combat aircraft (26 years) and would see more built (11,496) than any other jet in history. During the Vietnam War, they destroyed more than 120

American aircraft and scored victories in combat over India, Syria, Egypt, Iraq and Yugoslavia. In the 1970s, the U.S. acquired MiG-21s for evaluation, resulting in an elite Air Force unit called the "Red Eagles." This squadron of U.S. operated MiGs provided a realistic enemy to fight in aerial war games.

The Museum's MiG-21 is painted to resemble a Red Eagles aircraft. Built for the Polish Air Force, it was brought to the U.S. by Oscar Vickery and donated by George Gould in 2008.

Specifications

Type:	Fighter / Interceptor
First Flight:	February 14, 1955
Wingspan:	23 feet, 6 inches
Length:	47 feet, 7 inches
Height:	13 feet, 6 inches
Power:	One Tumanskiy R-13-300 afterburning turbojet
Crew:	1
Top Speed:	1,468 miles per hour (Mach 2.2)

KOREA AND VIETNAM ERA

Mikoyan MiG-23ML *Flogger-G*

In the struggle for air superiority in the Cold War, the Soviet Union sought to possess an aircraft that could deal with the American F-4 *Phantom II* on its own terms and win. While the earlier MiG-21 was good, it did not have range, weapons load, or advanced radar necessary to deal with the high-tech Western aircraft so the Mikoyan Design Bureau was tasked with fixing these deficiencies.

The MiG-23, which NATO codenamed "Flogger," was a whole new design for Mikoyan. It featured "swing wings"

for better performance at high and low speeds, as well as advanced "look down/ shoot down" radar. Entering service in 1967, the MiG-23 served with 33 different Soviet and aligned air forces and was produced in numbers well in excess of 5,000. A number of MiG-23s have been involved in combat over the Middle East, Afghanistan, and Africa.

The *Flogger-G*, is a second-generation MiG-23 that is lighter than earlier variants, has modern avionics and is optimized for air-to-air combat.

Specifications

Type:	Fighter
First Flight:	June 10, 1967
Wingspan:	45 feet, 10 inches
Length:	56 feet, 9.5 inches
Height:	15 feet, 10 inches
Power:	One Khatchaturov R-35-300 afterburning turbojet
Crew:	1
Top Speed:	840 miles per hour (Mach 1.14)

KOREA AND VIETNAM ERA

North American F-100F *Super Sabre*

Debuting in 1954, the F-100 *Super Sabre* was the first production jet fighter to maintain level supersonic flight. A replacement for the successful F-86 *Sabre*, the F-100 came to fame as an attack bomber in the skies over Vietnam during the early part of the war. Although replaced by F-105s and F-4s as a bomber, the *Super Sabre* still had a role to play. The F-model served as Forward Air Controllers known as *Misty FACs* in the dangerous job of spotting targets for other bombers. *Misty*s often drew heavy anti-aircraft fire while orbiting the targets, and casualty rates

were high. F-100s also served with other countries, including France, Denmark, Turkey and Taiwan and flew with the famous U.S. Air Force *Thunderbirds* aerobatic team for 12 years.

Restored at the Evergreen Maintenance Center, the Museum's *Super Sabre* honors General Merrill A. "Tony" McPeak; a *Misty FAC* pilot, an Oregon Aviation Hall of Honor inductee, and Air Force Chief of Staff during the 1990–91 Persian Gulf War.

Specifications

Type:	Fighter / Bomber
First Flight:	May 25, 1953
Wingspan:	38 feet, 95 inches
Length:	50 feet
Height:	16 feet, 3 inches
Power:	One Pratt & Whitney J57-P-21 afterburning turbojet
Crew:	2
Top Speed:	864 miles per hour (Mach 1.1)

KOREA AND VIETNAM ERA

North American FJ-3 *Fury*

First flown in 1946 with a straight wing, the original FJ-1 *Fury* saw little success due to its inadequate, low-powered jet engine. While North American was developing the *Fury* for the U.S. Navy, the Air Force asked them to modify it to a swept-winged version, resulting in the hugely successful F-86 *Sabre*. Seeing the difference the swept-wing made, the Navy bought a number of "navalized" *Sabres* under the designation FJ-2, as an interim measure. The FJ-3 *Fury*, which was in development at the time, also received a swept-wing like the F-86 and a far more powerful engine

that transformed it into viable fighter. It served with the U.S. Navy and Marine Corps as a fighter and bomber through the 1950s and 60s, with later versions being able to carry the Sidewinder missile; the first truly effective air-to-air missile.

This *Fury* is one of four known to exist and is on loan from the National Museum of the Marine Corps. It was restored by Evergreen Museum volunteers in 2005.

Specifications

Type:	Fighter
First Flight:	December 27, 1953
Wingspan:	37 feet, 2 inches
Length:	37 feet, 7 inches
Height:	13 feet, 7 inches
Power:	One Wright J65 turbojet
Crew:	1
Top Speed:	681 miles per hour

KOREA AND VIETNAM ERA

North American T-2C *Buckeye*

Specifications

With more and more jet aircraft coming into the inventory, the U.S. Navy issued a requirement in 1956 for a jet trainer that could be used to instruct student pilots from basic training through their carrier qualifications. North American Aviation won the contract based on a simple design utilizing elements of the FJ-1 *Fury* jet fighter and T-28 *Trojan* trainer. The *Buckeye* featured excellent visibility for both instructor and student, and a tail hook for carrier landings. The first version, the T-2A, had a single engine and was somewhat under-powered. Beginning in 1968, the Navy took delivery of the T-2B and later the T-2C, which corrected this with a two engine design. Virtually every naval aviator from 1960 through 2003 trained on the *Buckeye* at some point in his or her career. *Buckeyes* were all built at a plant in Columbus, Ohio, and its name came from the mascot of the Ohio State University.

The Museum's T-2C *Buckeye* is on loan from the National Museum of the Naval Aviation.

Type:	Trainer
First Flight:	January, 1958
Wingspan:	38 feet, 2 inches
Length:	38 feet, 8 inches
Height:	14 feet, 9 inches
Power:	Two General Electric J85-GE-4 turbojets
Crew:	2
Top Speed:	530 miles per hour

KOREA AND VIETNAM ERA

Northrop F-5E *Tiger II*

The F-5 started life as a variant of the T-38A *Talon* supersonic jet trainer, which was built in quantity for the U.S. Air Force. Utilizing profits from that program, Northrop took the daring step of creating a lightweight fighter based on the *Talon* as a private venture. Quickly seeing the value of it, the Defense Department acquired hundreds of these aircraft, dubbed the F-5A *Freedom Fighter*, to supply to anti-communist allies.

In 1972, Northrop introduced a higher performance model designated the F-5E

Tiger II. With a larger wing, longer fuselage, more powerful engines and an advanced radar system, the *Tiger II* was similar in size and capability to the Soviet MiG-21. This made it a perfect aircraft for the U.S. Air Force's Aggressor Squadrons, which "fought" other Air Force squadrons in exercises over the Nevada desert that provided a realistic air combat experience.

This aircraft is on loan from the National Museum of Naval Aviation and is painted as a U.S. Air Force Aggressor.

Specifications

Type:	Fighter
First Flight:	August 11, 1972
Wingspan:	26 feet, 82 inches
Length:	47 feet, 58 inches
Height:	13 feet, 5 inches
Power:	Two General Electric J85-GE-21B afterburning turbojets
Crew:	1
Top Speed:	1,060 miles per hour (Mach 1.6)

KOREA AND VIETNAM ERA

■ **Northrop** T-38A *Talon*

By the end of the 1950s, the U.S. Air Force still did not possess a trainer capable of Mach 1. At the same time, Northrop had developed the N-156 lightweight fighter design on its own, but it was slow to find customers. With some modification to the N-156, Northrop offered the Air Force a new trainer, which they eagerly accepted as the T-38.

The T-38A was the first supersonic trainer, and to date, the most produced. It is estimated that more than 50,000 U.S. and NATO pilots have trained

in the *Talon*, after learning the basics of flight in a T-37. In addition to its training role, the *Talon* was used by the world famous U.S. Air Force *Thunderbirds* precision flight demonstration team from 1974 to 1982, and has served NASA as a trainer and "taxi" for the astronauts since the mid-1960s.

This T-38A is on loan from the National Museum of the U.S. Air Force and is painted in NASA markings.

Specifications

Type:	Trainer
First Flight:	April 10, 1959
Wingspan:	25 feet, 3 inches
Length:	46 feet, 5 inches
Height:	12 feet, 11 inches
Power:	Two General Electric J85-5A afterburning turbojets
Crew:	2
Top Speed:	858 miles per hour (Mach 1.3)

KOREA AND VIETNAM ERA

Republic F-84F *Thunderstreak*

Specifications

Type:	Fighter / Bomber
First Flight:	June 3, 1950
Wingspan:	33 feet, 7 inches
Length:	43 feet, 5 inches
Height:	14 feet, 5 inches
Power:	One Wright J65-W-3 turbojet
Crew:	1
Top Speed:	695 miles per hour

During the Korean War, both the U.S. and Soviet Union put into practice the research done by German scientists in World War II regarding swept-wings and high performance flight. After seeing the tremendous performance advances of the swept-wing jets, Republic Aviation began work on converting their straight-wing F-84 *Thunderjet* into a high speed fighter. Started in 1949, the project ran into many difficulties and the *Thunderstreak* was not ready until after the Korean War ended. It was the first single-seat aircraft capable of carrying a nuclear weapon and was supplied to many NATO air forces including France, Germany, Italy, Greece and Turkey. One version was converted for photo reconnaissance work, being dubbed the *Thunderflash*. French F-84Fs were the only ones to see combat, destroying 20 Egyptian aircraft in the 1956 Suez Crisis.

This *Thunderstreak* was used by an aviation tech school in Iowa, before being restored by the Museum's restoration center and placed on display in 2009.

Republic F-105G *Thunderchief*

Designed to fly at supersonic speeds at a low altitude, the Republic F-105G *Thunderchief* was the largest single-engine fighter ever used by the U.S. Air Force. Although its original mission was to carry a nuclear weapon, the *Thunderchief* carried the brunt of the tactical bombing campaign in the Vietnam War until losses became too high.

In order to combat enemy Surface-to-Air (SAM) missiles that were destroying so many F-105s, the G-model was fitted with special electronics and radar-homing missiles to destroy the SAM launch sites. Codenamed "Wild Weasel," these missions were extremely dangerous. When the SAM site would track the *Wild Weasel* with its radar, the aircraft would shoot a homing missile that followed the radar beam back to its source to destroy the missile site. Additionally, they carried bombs to finish the job if necessary.

This F-105G *Thunderchief* is on loan from the National Museum of the United States Air Force.

Specifications

Type:	Fighter / Bomber
First Flight:	October 2, 1955
Wingspan:	34 feet, 11 inches
Length:	64 feet, 5 inches
Height:	19 feet, 8 inches
Power:	One Pratt & Whitney J75-P-19W afterburning turbojet
Crew:	2
Top Speed:	1,372 miles per hour (Mach 2.08)

KOREA AND VIETNAM ERA

■ **Republic** RC-3 *Seabee*

Designed as an all-purpose sports aircraft, the Republic RC-3 *Seabee* was one of the most unique general aviation airplanes developed following World War II. Having land and water capabilities, it gave sportsmen entry to fishing and hunting areas previously inaccessible.

Designer Percival H. Spencer first created a version of the flying sport amphibian in 1937. After the war, Republic Aircraft hired him and bought the design rights for his aircraft. Among its unique features is a bow door, so

sport anglers could do a little fishing while at anchor.

This aircraft was wrecked in a water landing, and was restored by Museum volunteers and Jim Poel, director of the International *Seabee* Owners Club and restoration director for the Curtiss Air Museum. Poel said Evergreen's *Seabee* is one of the finest restored aircraft he has ever seen. The *Seabee* was placed on exhibit in 2006.

Specifications

Type:	Sport Amphibian Flying Boat
First Flight:	November 30, 1944
Wingspan:	37 feet, 8 inches
Length:	27 feet, 11 inches
Height:	9 feet, 7 inches
Power:	One Franklin 6A8-215-B8F air-cooled engine
Crew:	1
Capacity:	3 passengers
Top Speed:	117 miles per hour

KOREA AND VIETNAM ERA

Schweizer SGS 2-32

Inspired by Lindbergh's flight, Ernest, Paul and William Schweizer launched their first glider in 1930. Using the knowledge they had gained from building that glider, the brothers formed the Schweizer Metal Aircraft Company in Elmira, New York and continued developing glider designs. The brothers created the SGS 2-32 in 1962, which was nicknamed "the Cadillac of Gliders." Once classified as the world's highest-performance production glider, the 2-32 set many records for altitude and speed during the 1960s and 70s.

During the Vietnam War, Lockheed used the 2-32 as a basis for the powered quiet reconnaissance aircraft, the YO-3, which was virtually undetectable at heights over 1,000 feet. Under the designation X-26, several more 2-32s were operated by the U.S. Navy Test Pilot School. A total of 87 were built and 65 are still flying today.

This aircraft is on loan from the National Soaring Museum.

Specifications

Type:	Sailplane
First Flight:	1962
Wingspan:	57 feet
Length:	26 feet, 9 inches
Height:	9 feet, 3 inches
Power:	None
Crew:	1
Capacity:	1-2 passengers
Top Speed:	158 miles per hour

KOREA AND VIETNAM ERA

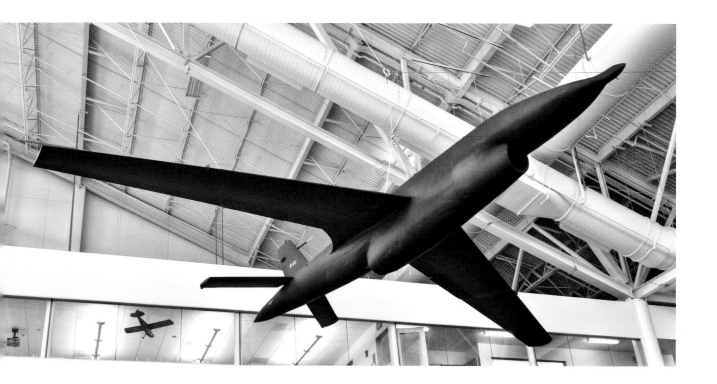

Teledyne-Ryan AQM-34N *Firebee*

At the height of the Cold War, both the East and West had closely-held military secrets, which were often heavily guarded. After the loss of a U-2 over the Soviet Union, the Air Force needed a new way to look at heavily defended targets without risking the lives of pilots, and they turned to the Teledyne-Ryan *Firebee* for a solution.

Originally designed as a remotely piloted target drone, the *Firebee* has undergone many modifications to take on many roles. The N-model *Firebee* was modified for reconnaissance.

Carrying a battery of cameras in the nose, the AQM-34N was launched from a DC-130 drone control aircraft and flown over targets of interest. On its return, it was caught in mid-air by a helicopter for re-use. *Firebee*s regularly overflew the Chinese nuclear test site at Lop Nor, and a number were lost; enough so that China reverse-engineered the *Firebee* and created their own identical copy, the Wu Zhen WZ-5.

This AQM-34N is on loan from the National Museum of the U.S. Air Force.

Specifications

Type:	Reconnaissance
First Flight:	1958
Wingspan:	32 feet
Length:	30 feet
Height:	5 feet, 7 inches
Power:	One Teledyne J69-T41A turbojet engine
Crew:	Unmanned
Top Speed:	420 miles per hour

Vought A-7D *Corsair II*

Originally designed as a replacement for the A-4 *Skyhawk* carrier-based attack aircraft, the A-7 *Corsair II* was one of the few designs to find success with both the Navy and the Air Force. Based on Vought's successful F-8 *Crusader*, the A-7 was shorter and lacked supersonic capability; but could carry up to 10 tons of bombs, rockets and missiles that it delivered with pin-point accuracy.

Pushed into ordering the aircraft by Robert McNamara, the Air Force found the A-7 to be an extremely capable attack platform. The D-model featured a more powerful engine and rotary cannon, which made it perfect for close air support. In Vietnam, Air Force A-7Ds supported search and rescue missions for downed aviators and flew the last U.S. air strike of the war. They continued to serve until the end of the first Gulf War with both the Navy and Air Force.

This A-7D is on loan from the National Museum of Naval Aviation and is painted in the markings of the 354th TFW while operating in Vietnam.

Type:	Attack
First Flight:	September 26, 1965
Wingspan:	38 feet, 9 inches
Length:	46 feet, 2 inches
Height:	16 feet, 1 inches
Power:	One Allison TF-41-A-1 turbofan
Crew:	1
Top Speed:	698 miles per hour

KOREA AND VIETNAM ERA

AVIATION TIMELINE

1946	1947	1950	1952	1953

January 26, 1946

Colonel William H. Council, piloting a Lockheed P-80 *Shooting Star*, makes a record breaking flight from Long Beach, California to LaGuardia, New York. It is the fastest crossing of the United States at the time, covering 2,470 miles in 4 hours at an average speed of 584 miles per hour.

October 14, 1947

Charles Yeager, a U.S. Air Force captain, is the first to break the sound barrier. Flying in the experimental rocket-powered Bell X-1, he reaches a speed of Mach 1.015 at an altitude of 45,000 feet.

December 17, 1950

The North American F-86 *Sabre*, or *Sabrejet*, engages in combat with Soviet MiG-15s over Korea. It is America's first swept wing fighter that can counter the similarly-winged MiG-15 in high speed dogfights. With a victory ratio of 10:1, F-86 pilots will be credited with shooting down 792 MiGs for a loss of only 78 *Sabre*s.

May 2, 1952

British Overseas Airways Corporation (BOAC) becomes the first airline to introduce a passenger jet, the de Havilland *Comet*. By introducing a jet plane to their airline, BOAC can fly at tremendous speeds, which cuts down travel time.

May 18, 1953

Jackie Cochran becomes the first woman to break the sound barrier. She flies a F-86 *Sabrejet* at an average speed of 652.337 miles per hour to reach Mach 1.

KOREA AND VIETNAM ERA

1955   1960   1962   1968   1969

November 1955

The Cessna 172 *Skyhawk* makes its appearance. A four-seat, single-engine, high-wing fixed-wing aircraft, the Cessna 172 will soon become the best selling four-seat aircraft in history due to its longevity and popularity.

December 30, 1960

McDonnell introduces the F-4 *Phantom II*. It will be used extensively during the Vietnam War, serving as the principal air superiority fighter for the U.S. Navy and Air Force. The *Phantom* will gain the legendary distinction of being the last U.S. fighter flown to attain ace status in the 20th Century.

October 14, 1962

The Lockheed U-2, a high-altitude aircraft of 70,000 feet, on a photo reconnaissance mission, captures photographic proof of Soviet missile bases under construction in Cuba. This will begin the 14-day Cuban Missile Crisis.

December 31, 1968

The Soviet Tupolev Tu-144 takes its first test flight. It is one of only two supersonic transport (SST) aircraft that enter commercial service, the other being the Anglo-French Concorde.

March 2, 1969

Aérospatiale-BAC Concorde, a turbojet-powered supersonic passenger airliner or SST, makes its first flight. It is a joint venture between Aérospatiale and the British Aircraft Corporation. Once entered into service, the Concorde will have continued commercial flights for 27 years.

KOREA AND VIETNAM ERA

The Modern Era

The last quarter of the 20th Century saw aviation woven into the fabric of everyday life, touching people on every corners of the planet. Every second, an airplane is taking off or landing somewhere in the world, carrying a precious cargo of people and goods in support of the global economy. Letters that used to take weeks to cross the country are now in hand overnight, and flying is not just for commerce or combat, but for fun! What humans struggled for centuries to achieve is now taken for granted, all because of the pioneers, who in years before, made the airplane a viable means of transportation.

Boeing 747-100

One of the most recognizable airliners in the world, the Boeing 747 revolutionized airline travel when it first entered service in 1970.

Dubbed a "Jumbo Jet," the 747 had its origins in a competition for a large military cargo aircraft. While the Boeing design did not win, it was re-introduced when Juan Trippe, the president of Pan American Airways, came to Boeing looking for an airliner twice the size of the airliners then in service. Driven by the rising demand for air travel in the 1960s, Pan Am wanted an aircraft that could carry 400 passengers at a distance of 5,000 miles.

The new aircraft was created not for passenger comfort, but rather because it was predicted that big, slow passenger jets like the 747 would soon be replaced by Supersonic Transports like the Concorde or Boeing's own SST. Engineers believed that most 747s would be relegated to carrying cargo, so the fuselage was designed to fit two rows of sea-going freight containers side by side. This also created the distinctive "hump" on the 747, because the cockpit was placed on a second deck, leaving the main deck open for cargo. The rear portion of the streamlined upper deck housed a first class lounge or more passengers.

Initially airports wondered if they could handle such a giant, but the 747 had no problems operating from the same airfields as earlier 707s or DC-8s. Its multiple landing gear legs and 18 tires distributed its 300-ton weight, while triple-slotted flaps and leading edge slats helped it land on existing runways with ease. One of the biggest issues, however,

THE MODERN ERA

was training pilots to operate from a cockpit three stories above the ground!

The 747 began service with a New York to London flight in January 1970, and since then, has maintained a remarkable record of safety and reliability. Throughout the next 40 years, the basic design was adapted to utilize several different engines and "stretched" three times to carry larger loads. One special version, designated VC-25, serves the President of the United States as Air Force One.

The Museum's 747 was built for Delta Airlines in 1970 and later flew with China Airlines and Pan Am before being purchased by Evergreen International Airlines and converted into a cargo freighter. It was flown into the McMinnville Municipal Airport in July 2009, and towed across the street to the Museum one week later. This same 747 now resides on top of Evergreen Wings & Waves Waterpark.

Specifications

Type:	Airliner / Cargo Freighter
First Flight:	February 9, 1969
Wingspan:	195 feet, 8 inches
Length:	231 feet, 10 inches
Height:	63 feet, 5 inches
Power:	Four Pratt & Whitney JT9D-7A turbofans
Crew:	3
Capacity:	Max. 452 passengers
Top Speed:	594 miles per hour

THE MODERN ERA

Aviat Christen *Eagle II*

Introduced by Frank Christensen in 1978, the *Eagle* set a new standard for homebuilt aircraft. Unable to buy out manufacturer Curtiss Pitts, Christensen based his new homebuilt airplane on the famous Pitts *Special.* The resulting *Eagle II* entered service as a two-place aerobatic machine for competition, advanced aerobatic training and sport cross-country flying. It has been incredibly popular with pilots worldwide, since aviation enthusiasts can build this high performance aircraft at home!

Selling for approximately $40,000, the aircraft consists of a series of 25 numbered "sub-kits," each containing separate sections of the aircraft with detailed instructions and diagrams. Unlike many homebuilt aircraft, the *Eagle II* has a completion rate of more than 90 percent, attesting to the innovative design philosophy that makes it a plane for everyone.

The Museum's *Eagle II* was built over the course of six years by James A. Poier and donated in 2002 after 18 years of flying. Poier passed away in 2005.

Specifications

Type:	Sport / Aerobatic
First Flight:	1978
Wingspan:	19 feet, 11 inches
Length:	17 feet, 11 inches
Height:	6 feet, 6 inches
Power:	One Lycoming AEIO 360 AID air-cooled engine
Capacity:	2
Top Speed:	184 miles per hour

THE MODERN ERA

■ Beechcraft *Starship* 2000A

A most striking aircraft, the Beechcraft *Starship* 2000 was created as a new generation business aircraft. Designer Burt Rutan was hired to help design the aircraft, which features a pusher layout, a variable sweep canard and tipsails in place of standard rudders for superior aerodynamic efficiency. Rutan's company, Scaled Composites, built an 85 percent sized proof-of-concept vehicle, which debuted in 1983 to positive reviews and promises that the full sized *Starship* would be FAA Certified by 1985.

Production of its advanced composite components proved difficult, however, and there were many issues with federal certification. These, plus the high purchase price, proved to be disastrous, and only 53 *Starship*s were made. Beech/Raytheon maintained ownership of most, and in 2003, announced a decision to reclaim and destroy the *Starship*s rather than to continue parts/technical support.

Only 12 aircraft were spared, and this one was donated by Raytheon in November 2003.

Type:	Executive Transport
First Flight:	February 15, 1986
Wingspan:	54 feet, 5 inches
Length:	46 feet, 1 inch
Height:	12 feet, 11 inches
Power:	Two Pratt & Whitney PT6A-67 turboprops
Crew:	2
Capacity:	8 passengers
Top Speed:	385 miles per hour

THE MODERN ERA

Glasair SH-2 RG

In 1980, the Glasair revolutionized the kit plane industry as the world's first pre-molded composite aircraft. Wishing to produce a quick-build kit for homebuilders, three Boeing Aircraft engineers founded the Stoddard-Hamilton Aircraft Company, later known as Glasair Aviation, in Arlington, Washington. With its pre-molded skin of sandwiched fiberglass, foam and fiberglass, the Glasair SH-2 was easy to build and proved to be very popular. It features exceptional range and great slow-speed handling, but also offers aerobatic capability, making it an appealing package for many homebuilders. Originally designed as a tail dragger, Glasair later incorporated retractable tricycle landing gear (hence the RG designation) and to date, over 3,000 Glasair kits have been produced.

When Frank Sigler built his Glasair SH-2 RG, he installed the standard 150 horsepower engine, but after a few test flights, he decided to replace it. It now features a 215-horsepower Lycoming engine, which gives it exceptional speed and performance. Completed in April 1986, Sigler donated it in 2002.

Specifications

Type:	Homebuilt
First Flight:	April 1986
Wingspan:	24 feet, 4 inches
Length:	19 feet, 6 inches
Height:	6 feet, 2 inches
Power:	One Lycoming, Model IO-360 AIA, air-cooled engine
Capacity:	2
Top Speed:	260 miles per hour

THE MODERN ERA

![logo] **Grumman** F-14D *Super Tomcat*

For more than three decades, the F-14 *Tomcat* served as the long-ranged defender of the U.S. Navy's fleets around the world. As an interceptor armed with the *Phoenix* missile, the F-14 was able to shoot down enemy aircraft at distances of more than 100 miles. *Tomcat*s went into combat in 1981 and 1989 with Libyan fighters over the Gulf of Sidra, where they scored four victories with no losses, and saw combat with the Iranian Air Force. The *Tomcat* also became an international "movie star" after being featured in the 1986 movie *Top Gun*. Twenty-five years after beginning production, Grumman offered the Navy the F-14 D-model, dubbed *Super Tomcat*, which featured far more powerful engines and a complete glass-cockpit with advanced avionics. The Navy procured 36 of these aircraft, 18 built new and 18 converted from older A-model *Tomcat*s.

This aircraft is one of the new-build F-14Ds, and flew combat missions during Operation Iraqi Freedom. It is on loan from the National Museum of Naval Aviation.

Specifications

Type:	Fighter / Interceptor
First Flight:	December 21, 1970
Wingspan:	64 feet (38 feet swept)
Length:	69 feet, 9 inches
Height:	16 feet
Power:	Two General Electric F110-GE-400 afterburning turbofans
Crew:	2
Top Speed:	1,544 miles per hour (Mach 2.34)

THE MODERN ERA

Handley *Raven*

Each year, millions of people attend airshows and watch with fascination as pilots perform seemingly impossible maneuvers with specially engineered aerobatic aircraft. Designed and built by Wayne Handley of Salinas, California, the spectacular *Raven* is a striking and exhilarating monoplane that dazzled air show crowds every time it took to the sky.

Beginning his acrobatic career flying a Pitts *Special* in competition and air shows, Handley transitioned to the *Raven* in 1990. The aircraft had exceptional performance and response to the controls for loops, rolls and precision aerobatic maneuvers.

A top air show performer, Handley flew the *Raven* for the last time on August 20, 2005, at the Northwest Antique Aircraft Air Show located at the McMinnville Municipal Airport. Following the show, he donated the aircraft to the Evergreen Museum.

Specifications

Type:	Aerobatic
First Flight:	1990
Wingspan:	24 feet, 6 inches
Length:	21 feet
Height:	6 feet
Power:	One Lycoming AIO540 air-cooled engine
Crew:	1
Top Speed:	220 miles per hour

THE MODERN ERA

■ **Insitu** A-20 *ScanEagle*

The Insitu A-20 *ScanEagle* is a new breed of unmanned aircraft that fly under the guidance of an operator up to 60 miles away. Using a computer and joystick, the operator radio coordinates to the *ScanEagle*, which calculates wind speed and direction to guide itself. The operator also controls the camera for real-time imagery. One of the advantages is that it needs no runway; launching from a catapult on a truck or small ship. At the end of its flight, it catches an arresting wire held aloft by poles.

Highly versatile, the *ScanEagle* is used in both civilian and military fields, including reconnaissance, oil platform patrol and anti-piracy operations, as well as wildlife and fire and ice flow tracking. With a flight time of up to 20 hours, it is an ideal observation platform and costs far less than traditional aircraft.

This Insitu A-20 *ScanEagle* is on loan from Evergreen International Aviation.

Specifications

Type:	Reconnaissance
First Flight:	June 19, 2002
Length:	11.8 feet
Height:	10.2 feet
Power:	One 3W 2-stroke piston engine
Crew:	Unmanned
Top Speed:	86.4 miles per hour

THE MODERN ERA

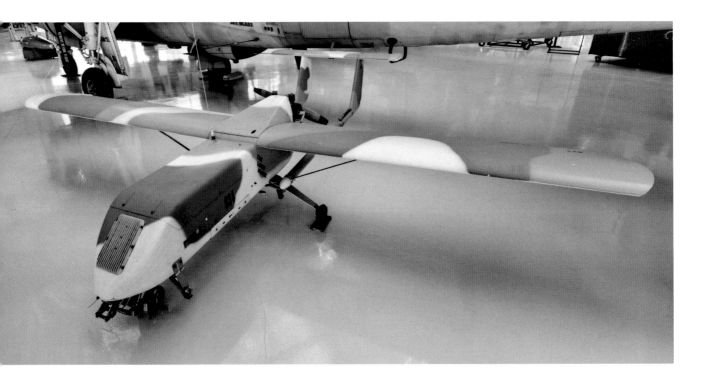

Israeli Aircraft Industries Mazlat *Mastiff* III

Produced by Tadiran in Israel, the *Mastiff* was part of the first generation of Unmanned Aerial Vehicles (UAVs), which used a television camera to provide real-time battlefield data. It was used by the Israeli military for locating missile sites in the Bekka Valley during the 1983 intervention in Lebanon. Able to loiter over the battlefield for long periods, *Mastiff*s assisted in the destruction of 28 Surface-to-Air (SAM) missile sites.

The U.S. Navy and Marine Corps quickly took an interest in the technology and acquired several *Mastiff* UAVs for testing from Mazlat, a corporate partnership between Tadiran and Israeli Aircraft Industries. These tests resulted in the development of the larger, more powerful *Pioneer* UAV, which was used to provide intelligence for U.S. commanders during the first Gulf War. *Mastiff*s remained in service with the Israeli Armed Forces through 1990.

This *Mastiff* III UAV is on loan from the National Museum of the Marine Corps.

Specifications

Type:	Reconnaissance
First Flight:	1973
Wingspan:	13 feet, 11 inches
Length:	10 feet, 10 inches
Height:	2 feet, 11 inches
Power:	One 22 hp piston engine
Crew:	Unmanned
Top Speed:	115 miles per hour

THE MODERN ERA

Lancair 360

Frustrated by his inability to find a kit plane he liked, Lance Neibauer decided to design his own. Neibauer started by asking homebuilders what features they were looking for in a homebuilt. The result was the Lancair; a high-performance aircraft that was among the first kit planes to feature molded composite construction. Pilots can construct the entire plane themselves or purchase a "Fastbuild Kit," which includes many manufactured components. Since 1984, more than 1,870 Lancair kits have been sold around the world.

Robert Hannay of Paradise Valley, Arizona purchased this Lancair 360 as a kit in 1988. Hannay and Pat Battle constructed the aircraft over a period of seven years and test flew it in 1995. This Lancair 360 is serial number 313 and does not incorporate the larger horizontal stabilizer of the "Big Tail" Lancair 360 MK II. The total estimated cost of construction for this Lancair 360 is more than $200,000. He donated it to the Museum in 2003.

Specifications

Type:	Homebuilt
First Flight:	April 1988
Wingspan:	23 feet, 6 inches
Length:	21 feet
Height:	6 feet, 5 inches
Power:	One Lycoming IO-360 engine
Crew:	2
Top Speed:	235 miles per hour

THE MODERN ERA

Learjet 24

Occasionally, a product becomes so universally used and well-regarded that its brand name becomes generic for that type of product. This is true for the Learjet, whose name is synonymous with personal luxury/executive travel.

The Learjet's origins are found in the design of a Swiss fighter plane from the 1950s, which failed to reach production. American inventor William Lear, creator of the car radio and 8-track tapes, purchased the tooling from the Swiss. Setting up a company in Wichita, Kansas, Lear created the world's first "business jet" designed for busy corporate executives who needed to travel in a hurry. The idea caught on, and the Learjet became the world's best selling executive jet. Throughout the years, the design has been stretched to accommodate more passengers, more fuel and more efficient engines, and is still in production today.

The Museum's Learjet 24 was donated in 2007 and painted to resemble an aircraft that serves with NASA at the Dryden Flight Research Center.

Specifications

Type:	Executive Transport
First Flight:	January 24, 1966
Wingspan:	35 feet, 7 inches
Length:	43 feet, 3 inches
Height:	12 feet, 3 inches
Power:	Two General Electric CJ610-6 turbojets
Crew:	2
Capacity:	5 passengers
Top Speed:	594 miles per hour

THE MODERN ERA

McDonnell Douglas F-15A *Eagle*

Designed from lessons learned in Vietnam where America's big, missile-armed fighters were vulnerable in dogfights with smaller, more nimble MiGs, the F-15 *Eagle* is a true modern dogfighter. Fast, powerful, maneuverable and armed with both missiles and guns, *Eagle*s have proven themselves the master of the dogfight. Flying for Israel, Saudi Arabia, Japan and the U.S. Air Force, F-15s have never lost a dogfight, having destroyed 104 enemy aircraft without a single loss.

The Museum's *Eagle* was manufactured

by McDonnell Douglas Aircraft in St. Louis, Missouri, and it was delivered to the U.S. Air Force on April 12, 1977. The National Museum of the U.S. Air Force loaned this F-15 *Eagle* to the Evergreen Aviation Museum in May 1996. Today the F-15 wears the squadron insignia of the Oregon Air National Guard and stands as a memorial to two F-15 pilots, Museum co-founder Captain Michael King Smith and Major Rhory Roger Draeger.

Specifications

Type:	Fighter
First Flight:	July 27, 1972
Wingspan:	42 feet, 10 inches
Length:	63 feet, 9 inches
Height:	18 feet, 8 inches
Power:	Two Pratt & Whitney F-100-PW-100 afterburning turbofan engines
Crew:	1
Top Speed:	1,875 mph

THE MODERN ERA

Mikoyan-Gurevich MiG-29 *Fulcrum A*

Developed in the midst of the Cold War, the MiG-29 was a response to advanced U.S. fighters such as the F-15 *Eagle* and F-16 *Fighting Falcon*. Its design began in the 1970s when the Soviets analyzed captured Western aircraft and used agents to buy or steal high technology systems. One of the most important was the radar, which was reportedly developed from that of an F-14 *Tomcat* the Soviets obtained from Iran. To make it more utilitarian, the MiG-29 was equipped with durable landing gear and intake grates, allowing it to operate from primitive airfields.

Consistently outperforming other fighters of its day, the MiG-29 became a force to be reckoned with. Many countries have procured the *Fulcrum*, including India, Iraq, Iran, Pakistan, Cuba, Peru and all Soviet Bloc nations. The *Fulcrum* saw combat with the Iraqi Air Force and with Yugoslavia in the Bosnian campaign. It remains a potent part of many world air forces.

This aircraft was donated to the Museum in 2007.

Specifications

Type:	Fighter
First Flight:	October 6, 1977
Wingspan:	37 feet, 3 inches
Length:	57 feet
Height:	15 feet, 6 inches
Power:	Two Klimov RD-33 afterburning turbofans
Crew:	1
Top Speed:	1,490 miles per hour (Mach 2.25)

THE MODERN ERA

Northrop-Grumman RQ-4A *Global Hawk* Mock-Up

Specifications

As operations of America's SR-71 *Blackbird* spy planes were winding down in the 1990s, a new vehicle was in development to take over the role of strategic reconnaissance, and it was very different. It had no pilot. The RQ-4 *Global Hawk* was created to meet a Defense Advanced Research Projects Agency (DARPA) requirement for a high altitude unmanned reconnaissance vehicle in 1995 and entered production in 2002, because of the extreme need for intelligence in Iraq and Afghanistan.

Capable of staying aloft for 36+ hours

at an altitude of 65,000 feet, the *Global Hawk* is controlled by three remote operators; an operator located at its launch point, an operator that flies the mission and a sensor operator. However, they are there more to monitor the aircraft, as it can take off, perform its mission and land autonomously. The RQ-4 communicates through a satellite antenna and can provide decision makers with real time data from radar, infrared, and electro-optical sensors.

This RQ-4A mock-up was donated by Northrop-Grumman in 2010.

Type:	Reconnaissance
First Flight:	February 1998
Wingspan:	116 feet, 2 inches
Length:	44 feet, 5 inches
Height:	15 feet, 2 inches
Power:	One Allison Rolls-Royce AE3007H turbofan engine
Crew:	Unmanned
Top Speed:	497 miles per hour

THE MODERN ERA

Oldfield *Baby Great Lakes*

Some pilots explain the *Baby Great Lakes* like this, "It might not be much to look at, but you should feel it fly!" A scaled down version of the *Great Lakes* 2T-1, the *Baby* has an unexpected high performance. For aerobatics, the *Baby* is stressed for 9 Gs; more than a World War II fighter. The *Baby Great Lakes* is a homebuilt, meaning that a pilot or enthusiast purchases plans and constructs the airplane in a garage or shop.

The Museum's *Baby Great Lakes* was built throughout a span of 27 years by

Earl Thorp of Moses Lake, Washington. As his creation neared completion in the fall of 1996, Thorp was injured in a car accident that left him unable to fly his homemade machine. Undaunted, he continued building. Upon completion in 1997, Thorpe asked his friend and former Big Bend Community College flight instructor, Buck Wheat, to take his *Baby* aloft. On the morning of August 12, 1997, this plane made its first and only flight. It was donated to the Museum in 1999.

Specifications

Type:	Homebuilt
First Flight:	1954
Wingspan:	16 feet, 8 inches
Length:	13 feet, 9 inches
Height:	4 feet, 6 inches
Power:	One Continental A-75 air-cooled engine
Crew:	1
Top Speed:	135 miles per hour

THE MODERN ERA

Pitts S-2B *Special*

The first Pitts *Special* biplane was created in 1944 by Florida crop duster Curtis Pitts. He wanted to design something more exciting than the old Stearman he flew over fields every day. By the 1960s, aerobatics flyers and their Pitts *Special*s were winning titles worldwide. Pitts *Special*s became known as one of the best stunt aircraft ever built. "The Pitts is ridiculously overpowered," explained one owner. "It can spin like a dervish, roll like a log and turn on a dime." Many solo aerobatics champions and demonstration teams, such as Canada's *Carling Red Tops*,

England's *Rothmans Aerobatic Team* and the *Jordanian Royal Falcons* fly Pitts *Special*s.

Purchased by Evergreen, this aircraft became a favorite of Michael King Smith. An expert pilot, Smith often flew the speedy little aircraft in air show performances. With its hot rod performance, small stature and large engine, the Pitts was a thrill to the young man who raced cars and flew fighters.

Specifications

Type:	Aerobatics
First Flight:	September 1944
Wingspan:	20 feet
Length:	18 feet, 9 inches
Height:	6 feet, 8 inches
Power:	One Textron Lycoming AEIO-540-D4A5 air-cooled engine
Crew:	2
Top Speed:	210 miles per hour

THE MODERN ERA

Quickie Q2

One of dozens of unconventional aircraft designed by famed aviation engineer Burt Rutan, the Quickie Q2 appears to be a canard design, but is actually a tandem wing aircraft. The front wing carries the elevators and landing gear and provides approximately 60 percent of the lift, while the rear wing acts as a horizontal stabilizer. This means the tail can be much more slender, creating less drag. A highly efficient design, Rutan said he was inspired by the X-Wing fighter from *Star Wars*.

The original Quickie design was a single-seater, but within four years of its introduction, a two seat version of the Q2 was available to homebuilders who wanted to fly with a friend. The Quickie series was created to be an attractive, exciting, simple design for the first time homebuilder and over 2,000 kits were manufactured before the Quickie Aircraft Company ceased operation.

This Quickie Q2 was built by Greg Kelsey and Amos Garrison of Boise, Idaho and flown for 25 years before its donation to the Museum in 2009.

Specifications

Type:	Homebuilt
First Flight:	1978
Wingspan:	16 feet, 8 inches
Length:	19 feet, 10 inches
Height:	4 feet, 5 inches
Power:	One Revmaster 2100-DQ air-cooled engine
Capacity:	2
Top Speed:	180 miles per hour

THE MODERN ERA

Thorp T-18 3BF *Tiger*

John Thorp created the T-18 to be one of the first fully metal, homebuilt aircraft. It became one of the world's most popular homebuilts, with its high performance and sleek, fighter-like looks. Originally designed as an open cockpit aircraft centered on a military surplus generator engine, it was found to have excellent performance, and the addition of a streamlined cowling and the bubble canopy made it even better. Some builders have even built their T-18s with retractable landing gear.

The T-18 was the first homebuilt to achieve 200 mph, and the first to utilize the "all flying" stabilator, commonly found on high-performance jets. The T-18 was also the first homebuilt to circumnavigate the world and fly to the North Pole. And, for those who want to build their own *Tiger*, the good news is that kits with laser cut parts are still in production!

Dr. Robert G. Furrer spent 14 years constructing this aircraft before donating it to the Museum in July 2008.

Specifications

Type:	Sport / Homebuilt
First Flight:	1963
Wingspan:	20 feet, 10 inches
Length:	18 feet, 10 inches
Height:	5 feet, 1 inch
Power:	One Lycoming O-360 air-cooled engine
Crew:	2
Top Speed:	200 miles per hour

THE MODERN ERA

Van's Aircraft RV-6

Specifications

Type:	Homebuilt
First Flight:	June 1985
Wingspan:	23 feet
Length:	20 feet, 2 inches
Height:	5 feet, 3 inches
Power:	Various 150-180 hp air-cooled piston engines
Capacity:	2
Top Speed:	198 miles per hour

Following a tradition of homebuilding in Oregon that began in the 1930s, Richard "Van" VanGrunsven set out in the 1970s to create a high performance homebuilt airplane. The result was the RV-3; a single-seater that was nimble, had great short-field performance and was fast! Realizing many people were willing to build an airplane like his, Van started offering partial kits.

From the RV-3, the design evolved to the RV-4; a two passenger, tandem design, and then, the RV-6 with side-by-side seating in 1985. While Van was concerned that widening the fuselage would cause a performance loss, it turned out that the RV-6 was only three miles per hour slower than the RV-4. The wider fuselage also allowed for baggage stowage and increased fuel capacity. Listening to the input of pilots and builders, Van's also added options for tricycle landing gear and a sliding canopy. To date over 2,400 RV-6s have been built and flown.

This aircraft is a RV-6, #1, and retained as an engineering prototype. It was donated by Richard VanGrunsven.

THE MODERN ERA

Yakovlev Yak-50

Created by Soviet aircraft designer Alexander Sergeevich Yakovlev, the Yak-50 is a single-seat, low wing competition aerobatic airplane. Never introduced directly into Russian military service, it was used for training at Soviet state-sponsored aviation clubs.

It was first flown in 1975, and proved its aerobatic versatility at the 1976 World Aerobatic Championships where Yak-50s took the first, second and fifth places in the men's competition and the top five places in the women's event. When they were made available for sale in the West, Yak-50s were eagerly acquired by those looking for a low-priced, high performance machine. As Royal Air Force commander Sir John Allison described flying it, the Yak-50 was "a comparable experience to a World War II fighter at a fraction of the cost."

This Yak-50 was a standby aircraft for the Soviet National Aero Team, and was later purchased by Bill Reesman as part of a civilian aerobatic team called "YAK Attack." The Museum acquired it in 2001.

Specifications

Type:	Sport / Aerobatics
First Flight:	1975
Wingspan:	31 feet, 2 inches
Length:	25 feet, 7 inches
Height:	10 feet, 6 inches
Power:	One Vedeneyev M-14P radial engine
Crew:	1
Top Speed:	249 miles per hour

THE MODERN ERA

1970   1976   1979   1986   1988

January 22, 1970

The Boeing 747, the first jumbo jet ever produced, enters service for Pan Am's New York-London route. The 747 will hold the passenger capacity record for a seating of more than 366 for 37 years.

July 27, 1976

The Lockheed SR-71 *Blackbird*, flown by Eldon W. Joersz and George T. Morgan Jr., sets the current record for the highest airspeed attained by an aircraft with a speed of 2,193 miles per hour.

June 12, 1979

Bryan Allen flies the *Gossamer Albatross* from Folkestone, England to Cap Gris-Nez, France, completing the first man-powered flight to cross the English Channel.

December 23, 1986

Richard Rutan and Jeana Yeager, two U.S. pilots, complete the first nonstop flight around the world without refueling. They fly in the Rutan Model 76 *Voyager* for 216 hours, covering 24,987 miles.

December 21, 1988

The Russian Antonov An-225 *Mriya*, the world's heaviest aircraft, makes its first flight. As a strategic airlift cargo aircraft, the Antonov is in commercial operation and carries oversized payloads.

THE MODERN ERA

1991

1998

2001

2002

2007

January 17, 1991

The Lockheed F-117 *Nighthawk*, the first operational aircraft designed around stealth technology, makes its first successful combat sortie in Operation Desert Storm, destroying an Iraqi telecommunications facility.

August 21, 1998

An Insitu Aerosonde named *Laima* becomes the first UAV to cross the Atlantic Ocean, completing the flight in 26 hours.

April 24, 2001

The UAV RQ-4 *Global Hawk* completes the longest point-to-point flight made by an unmanned aircraft when it crosses the Pacific Ocean from the U.S. to land in Australia in 23 hours.

July 3, 2002

Steve Fossett of the United States makes the first solo nonstop round-the-world balloon flight. Completing his flight in 14 days and 19 hours, Fossett also breaks 3 balloon records with the fastest time around the world, longest distance flown solo, and longest time flown solo.

October 25, 2007

The largest passenger airliner, the Airbus A380, goes into commercial service for Singapore Airlines. It is a double-deck, wide-body, four-engine jet airliner and due to its size, many airports have to modify facilities to accommodate the A380.

THE MODERN ERA

THE EVERGREEN STORY

Top Above: Evergreen B212, over the oil fields of Kuwait. Evergreen aircraft served as a lifeline for Kuwait following Desert Shield/Desert Storm.

Above: Evergreen Trade Inc has been "Matching Machines to Missions" for more than 50 years.

Right: An Evergreen B-747 freighter touches down in Petropavlovsk, Russia.

The Evergreen Story

Recognized as one of the most respected aviation service companies in the world for the last 50 years, Evergreen International Aviation and its subsidiaries employ more than 5,000 personnel who have served customers in more than 170 countries. The company has always resolved to perform safely and reliably in every endeavor that it has undertaken. Evergreen aims to make its quality services tangible to our customers at the most economical cost.

Integrated services from Evergreen's diverse subsidiaries enhance all of its operations and synergistically combine to tackle the toughest missions and fulfill the most demanding requirements. No matter the job, Evergreen will perform it safely and dependably.

Evergreen International Aviation's subsidiaries include Evergreen Helicopters; Evergreen International Airlines; Evergreen Aviation Ground Logistics Enterprise; Evergreen Trade; and Evergreen Agricultural Enterprises. While Evergreen has great pride in its accomplishments, the company is always focusing on the future. Evergreen will continue to play a pivotal role in the economic stability and development of the aviation and commerce industries throughout this century. It has determined that its role be one of leadership, quality and commitment to its customers, business associates and employees.

THE EVERGREEN STORY

Rotary Wing Flight

The dream of taking off and landing vertically has been around for centuries, as seen in the toys of China and Renaissance Europe. But it was not until Igor Sikorsky developed the first practical helicopter in 1939 that the dream was in the grasp of humanity. Pushed by the needs of battle, the helicopter transformed the way wars were fought. Today, the helicopter has become indispensable as an air ambulance, a search and rescue tool, a transport to inaccessible places and even the ultimate "chairlift" for skiers. Like fixed wing airplanes, the helicopter has become a part of everyday life for people around the globe.

Hiller UH-12E3 *Raven*

With no need for runways, helicopters have many advantages over fixed-wing aircraft for work in agriculture, construction, forestry and petroleum exploration. They can fly to spots where even ground vehicles are unable to go, transporting people, equipment and materials necessary to get a job done. An industrial "workhorse" involved in aerial spraying, seeding, timber transport, law enforcement and rescue work, the Hiller 360/UH-12 was the first all-metal light helicopter in the civilian market.

Stanley Hiller was always an innovator

and his helicopter designs "pushed the envelope" of rotary wing technology. He designed his first successful helicopter at the age of 19, and a year later, with the help of industrialist Henry Kaiser, he founded United Helicopters in 1946. The UH-12 was his first mass-produced helicopter, and it found a receptive market with both civilian operators and the military. Hiller used a flair for the dramatic to sell helicopters, including a hands-off flying demonstration where he stood outside the helicopter, and the first trans-continental flight of a helicopter in 1949. All of this helped to

focus attention on the capabilities of the helicopter, which prior to that time had seen only limited use.

In military service, these utility "choppers" were used for training and observation, while some were mounted with guns to act as forward scouts. During the Korean War, litter-equipped *Raven*s saved the lives of many wounded soldiers by transporting them to Mobile Army Surgical Hospital (MASH) units. Eventually they would serve with the U.S. Army, the U.S. Navy and 17 other air forces around the world. Many

ROTARY WING FLIGHT

civilian and military UH-12s are still flying today.

This Hiller UH-12E is one of two Hillers with which aviator-pioneer Delford M. Smith founded Evergreen Helicopters, Inc. in the early 1960s. Equipped with the patented "PaceSpreader" technology developed by Evergreen for precise application of seed or dry chemical fertilizers, UH-12s were involved in tree seeding and forest fertilization projects that would have been economically impossible without the helicopter. Evergreen's Hiller 12Es

also provided many other services, such as aerial inventory (from counting moose to cars on the road), dredging, firefighting, medical evacuation and transport, news casting, off-loading barges, photography, support for construction, power line and seismic work, and search and rescue.

By proving the worth and importance of using helicopters, Evergreen eventually became the world's largest operator of Hiller 12Es.

Type:	Utility
First Flight:	November 1947
Rotorspan:	25 feet, 3 inches
Length:	28 feet, 11 inches
Height:	6 feet, 3 inches
Power:	One Lycoming VO-540-A1A air-cooled engine
Crew:	1-3
Top Speed:	95 miles per hour

ROTARY WING FLIGHT

■ **Bell** 206 *Jet Ranger*

In 1960, Bell was one of 12 manufacturers who submitted designs for a U.S. Army request for a new light observation helicopter. Having lost the competition, Bell redesigned their Model 206 to have a better cargo/passenger capacity and a more aesthetically pleasing look and presented it to the civilian market. It became an immediate hit as a transport for business executives, an "eye in the sky" for police departments, and a vehicle for sight-seeing tour operators.

As the *Jet Ranger*'s popularity took off

in the civil market, the military took another look at it and the U.S. Navy decided to procure it as the TH-57 *Sea Ranger* for basic helicopter training. The Army then followed suit and acquired them as light observation scout helicopters under the designation OH-57 *Kiowa*. Today, the military forces of over 50 countries and countless civilian users operate variants of the Bell 206.

This Bell 206 was used by Evergreen Helicopters of Alaska and was loaned to the Museum when it was retired from service.

Specifications

Type:	Utility
First Flight:	January 10, 1966
Rotorspan:	33 feet, 8 inches
Length:	39 feet, 4 inches
Height:	9 feet, 4 inches
Power:	One Allison C250-20J turboshaft engine
Crew:	1
Capacity:	4 passengers
Top Speed:	139 miles per hour

ROTARY WING FLIGHT

Bell AH-1F *Cobra*

While the helicopter had proven to be an indispensable mode of transport during the Korean War, it was in Vietnam that the helicopter became master of the battlefield. Much of this was because of the Bell AH-1 *Cobra*, the first helicopter designed from the start as a flying gun platform.

First flown in 1965, the *Cobra* was designed to provide fast, mobile, close air support for troops in combat and to provide an escort for troop carrying helicopters. It utilized components from the UH-1 *Iroquois* (Huey),

including the engine, transmission, rotor and tail, which helped to speed its development and entry into service. Based on combat experience, the *Cobra* design was updated with armored glass, a higher performance engine and all-weather capabilities. Later, *Cobra*s such as this AH-1F were equipped with TOW missiles for anti-tank operations. *Cobra*s have served with the U.S. Army, Marines and many foreign air forces.

This aircraft is on loan from the U.S. Army Tank and Automotive Command.

Type:	Attack
First Flight:	September 7, 1965
Rotorspan:	44 feet
Length:	44 feet, 7 inches
Height:	13 feet, 6 inches
Power:	One Avco Lycoming T53-L-703 turboshaft
Crew:	2
Top Speed:	172 miles per hour

ROTARY WING FLIGHT

Bell HTL-3

Between 1947 and 1958, the U.S. Navy procured a number of Bell helicopters for use as trainers and utility duties, recognizing that the helicopter could be a valuable tool aboard ships at sea or on shore. In 1947, the Navy borrowed 10 Bell Model 47As from the U.S. Air Force for testing and evaluation, which were designated HTLs. Pleased with the results, they ordered the HTL-3 as an advanced version with a more powerful engine and an enclosed fuselage. Nine were purchased and the Navy loaned examples to both the Coast Guard and the Marine Corps for combat

evacuation. Three others were sold to Brazil. During the Korean War, the little helicopters flew with Marine squadron VMO-6 and were used for artillery spotting, observation and casualty evacuation.

This HTL-3 saw combat in Korea with VMO-6, flying 149 missions, and of the 12 HTL-3's built, it is the only one known to still exist in North America. It was restored by Jack Lenhardt and placed on display in 2003 by Delford M. Smith.

Specifications

Type:	Utility
First Flight:	December 8, 1945
Rotorspan:	37 feet, 2 inches
Length:	31 feet, 6 inches
Height:	9 feet, 7 inches
Power:	One Franklin 6V4-200-C32 air-cooled engine
Crew:	2
Top Speed:	105 miles per hour

ROTARY WING FLIGHT

Bell OH-13E *Sioux*

When most people think of small helicopters, they think of a Bell Model 47. The military version of the Model 47, the OH-13 was a rugged, general purpose observation and utility helicopter that was also quickly pressed into service as a flying ambulance. Coming into widespread use in Korea in January 1951, just a few months after the outbreak of the war, its skid-type landing gear proved a good platform for stretchers, although the doors had to be removed with that use. Subsequent models used a "cut-out" on the door to permit opening the door with the

stretchers in place. This model became famous due to its regular appearance on the television show *M.A.S.H.*

Before production ended, the OH-13 and Model 47 served in the military forces of 42 different countries, and all branches of the U.S. military, as well as an uncounted number of civilian users. Because of the demand for these light helicopters, Bell licensed production to Westland in Great Britain and Agusta in Italy.

Specifications

Type:	Utility
First Flight:	December 8, 1945
Rotorspan:	37 feet, 2 inches
Length:	31 feet, 6 inches
Height:	9 feet, 7 inches
Power:	One Franklin 6V4-200-C32 air-cooled engine
Crew:	2
Top Speed:	105 miles per hour

ROTARY WING FLIGHT

Bell UH-1H *Iroquois*

Perhaps no other aircraft is as closely associated with the Vietnam War as the Bell UH-1 *Iroquois*. Popularly called the "Huey", its widespread use made it a symbol of the war in the minds of the public. Created as utility helicopters, they were tasked with troop and supply transport, medical evacuation, convoy escort, waterway patrol and even as gunships. In their role as flying ambulances, these Hueys could hold up to six stretchers, as well as three medical personnel. The most numerous were the H-model, with over 5,000 produced. Hueys have served with air forces in more than 65 countries, as well as many civilian operators.

This helicopter, serial number 64-13502, provided years of service toward fulfilling the mission of the Oregon Army National Guard. After being overhauled from crash damage in 1967, it served in Corpus Christi, Texas and Phoenix, Arizona, before going to the Oregon Army National Guard in 1986. It was retired from service in September 1994, and is on loan from the U.S. Army's Tank and Automotive Command.

Specifications	
Type:	Transport
First Flight:	October 22, 1956
Rotorspan:	48 feet
Length:	42.7 feet
Height:	14.7 feet
Power:	One Lycoming T53-L-13 turbine engine
Crew:	2-3
Capacity:	12-15 passengers or 6 stretchers
Top Speed:	145 miles per hour

ROTARY WING FLIGHT

■ **Hiller** 1031 *Flying Platform* Replica

Ever since *One Thousand and One Arabian Nights*, people have been intrigued by flying carpets. While this has never become a reality, it came close when Stanley Hiller built his *Flying Platform*. It began with Charles Zimmerman, who developed a vertical take-off rig called "Flying Shoes," consisting of a platform with two engines the pilot would strap to his feet. To move in one direction or another, the pilot shifted his weight in the direction he wanted to go, similar to riding a bike.

Hiller acquired the design and mated the control concept with a ducted fan to meet a Navy proposal. The Model 1031 *Flying Platform* was developed in secret and featured a ring structure that ducted the thrust from the propellers downward to create lift. The Army became interested in it as a way to move over mine fields or provide a platform for sharp-shooters, and although several versions were tested, the Army lost interest and the project was abandoned.

This replica of the Hiller 1031 *Flying Platform* was built by Ken Spence of Bend, Oregon in 2006.

Specifications

Type:	Experimental
First Flight:	1955
Rotorspan:	8 feet, 4 inches
Length:	7 feet
Height:	7 feet
Power:	Two Nelson H-59 two-cycle, 40 horsepower engines
Crew:	1
Top Speed:	16 miles per hour

ROTARY WING FLIGHT

Hiller H-23B *Raven*

Swooping down from the sky to pick up a wounded soldier on the battlefield, the Hiller H-23 *Raven*, was less like a blackbird and more like an angel of mercy. The ability to move casualties from the battlefield to a Mobile Army Surgical Hospital (MASH) raised the chances of survival for wounded soldiers and saved countless lives. Derived from the civilian UH-12, the H-23 was one of the U.S. Army's first helicopters equipped for utility, observation and medical evacuation, and it saw widespread use in the Korean War.

The *Raven* would also serve the Army well through the 1950s as a trainer, teaching many pilots to fly helicopters. More than half of all the OH-23Bs were used as trainers at Fort Wolters, Texas. When the Army went to war in Vietnam, the *Raven* was equipped with guns and used as forward scouts, until replaced by the much faster OH-6 *Cayuse*.

Restored by Jack Lenhardt, this OH-23B joined the Museum's collection in 2003 via Delford M. Smith, founder of Evergreen International Aviation.

Specifications

Type:	Utility
First Flight:	November 1947
Rotorspan:	25 feet, 3 inches
Length:	28 feet, 11 inches
Height:	8 feet, 3 inches
Power:	One Lycoming HIO-360-D14 air-cooled engine
Crew:	3
Top Speed:	84 miles per hour

ROTARY WING FLIGHT

Hiller YROE-1 *Rotorcycle*

Specifications

During the Korean War, aircrews shot down in enemy territory faced almost certain capture, but rotary-winged aircraft offered a chance for escape, especially with the trend toward smaller and lighter helicopters during the early 1950s. Encouraged by the helicopter's potential, the Navy Bureau of Aeronautics requested proposals for a one-man self-rescue helicopter. Hiller Helicopters, led by the innovative Stanley Hiller, won the contract in 1954 with a novel, collapsible helicopter.

Weighing only 290 pounds and measuring 27 inches in diameter when folded, the *Rotorcycle* was small enough to fit into a pod dropped by parachute to a pilot waiting below. The *Rotorcycle* featured rapid assembly with no tools, enabling a downed pilot to escape and evade an enemy. However, a lack of visual reference on the structure made it hard to fly and the Marine Corps cancelled testing before it entered service, halting production at 12 examples.

This *Rotorcycle* is on loan from Stephen Hiller and the Hiller Aviation Museum.

Type:	Rescue
First Flight:	January 10, 1957
Rotorspan:	18 feet, 6 inches
Length:	12 feet, 6 inches
Height:	7 feet, 6 inches
Power:	One Nelson YO-65-2, four-cylinder, two-cycle engine
Crew:	1
Top Speed:	70 miles per hour

ROTARY WING FLIGHT

Hughes 269A *Osage*

In the mid-1950s, helicopters had improved to the point that some people believed there might soon be a "chopper" in every garage. Hughes Aircraft aimed to fill that market with the lightweight, low cost Model 269. Used by television and radio stations, utility and oil companies, construction firms, farmers, ranchers and charter air taxi services, the Model 269 was major success. The U.S. Army used them as trainers under the designation TH-55A *Osage*.

In 1956, two prototype Model 269s

were built. This is the second one, with the serial number 0002, which was used to re-engineer the helicopter line for easier production and maintenance. This second prototype was reworked with a tubular boom to replace the original truss-work tail and was fitted with an improved and strengthened cockpit enclosure. Howard Hughes is rumored to have flown it for personal use. It was acquired in 1991 and displayed in 1997.

Specifications

Type:	Utility
First Flight:	October 2, 1956
Rotorspan:	25 feet
Length:	23 feet, 2 inches
Height:	7 feet, 11 inches
Power:	One Lycoming HIO-360-D14 engine
Crew:	2
Top Speed:	90 miles per hour

ROTARY WING FLIGHT

Hughes 500D

The Hughes 500 helicopter was originally created to meet a 1963 U.S. Army requirement for a Light Observation Helicopter (LOH), and was successfully employed in Vietnam and beyond as the OH-6 *Cayuse*. This fast, light helicopter was used as an aero-scout, working ahead of an assault group to probe for the enemy; a job that was dangerous and had a high casualty rate.

Because of the speed, ruggedness and dependability that made it a good scout, the Hughes 500 became a favorite in the civilian market as well. The 500D was

introduced in 1976, featuring a more powerful engine, a 5-blade main rotor and a "T-tail." Evergreen International has partnered with the World Health Organization since 1974, using Hughes 500s to spray for the black fly, which causes river blindness, and has protected over 30 million people in 13 African countries from the dreaded disease.

The Hughes 500D on display is on loan from Evergreen Helicopters and took part in the river blindness eradication project.

Type:	Utility
First Flight:	February 27, 1963
Rotorspan:	26 feet, 4 inches
Length:	30 feet, 10 inches
Height:	8 feet, 2 inches
Power:	One Allison 250-C20 turboshaft engine
Crew:	2
Capacity:	3 passengers
Top Speed:	175 miles per hour

ROTARY WING FLIGHT

■ **Kaman** SH-2F *Seasprite*

Designed for use on the confined decks of U.S. Navy destroyers, the *Seasprite* is a compact helicopter which features folding rotor blades to reduce its length. Originally assigned search and rescue and utility missions, the *Seasprite* was later adapted for anti-submarine warfare. As an integral part of every naval task force, the *Seasprite*s provided a ring of submarine protection around the ships with a variety of sensors and weapons including homing torpedoes.

Kaman delivered 190 *Seasprite*s beginning in 1962, and they flew many

search and rescue missions for downed aviators in Vietnam. As such, they were armed for dangerous missions, deep in enemy territory. The first variants used a single engine, but beginning with the C-model, the *Seasprite* received two engines for greater reliability. They remained in service through 1993 with the U.S. Navy, but additional examples continued to fly for New Zealand.

This SH-2F *Seasprite* is on loan from the National Museum of Naval Aviation.

Specifications

Type:	Utility
First Flight:	July 2, 1959
Rotorspan:	44 feet
Length:	52 feet, 2 inches
Height:	13 feet, 6 inches
Power:	Two General Electric T58-GE-8F turboshaft engine
Crew:	4
Top Speed:	162 miles per hour

ROTARY WING FLIGHT

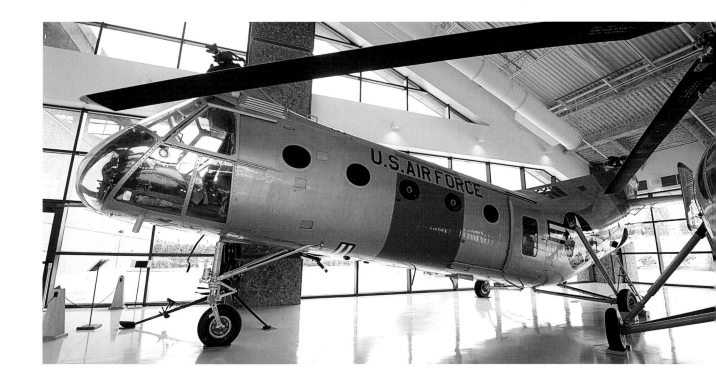

Piasecki H-21C *Shawnee*

One of the biggest problems with controlling helicopters is the need to counteract the torque from the spinning blades. Most use a tail rotor, but Piasecki chose tandem rotors, turning in opposite directions to cancel torque. All of the engine power could go to generating lift, giving Piasecki designs an advantage for the military's "heavy lift" needs.

The H-21 was designed to the Air Force's need for a rescue helicopter suited to Arctic conditions and was based off an earlier Navy design. It inherited the upward angle of the rear fuselage, which kept the rotors from hitting one another and earned the nickname "Flying Banana." The Air Force utilized the H-21 to build the early warning radar stations of the DEW Line in Alaska and northern Canada. The U.S. Army bought the H-21 for use as an assault transport, which they named *Shawnee*, and many were used in the early years of the Vietnam War.

This H-21C *Shawnee* is on loan from the National Museum of the United States Air Force.

Specifications

Type:	Cargo
First Flight:	April 1952
Rotorspan:	44 feet
Length:	52 feet, 6 inches
Height:	15 feet, 9 inches
Power:	One Wright R-1820-103 radial engine
Crew:	3-5
Capacity:	20 passengers or 12 stretchers
Top Speed:	127 miles per hour

ROTARY WING FLIGHT

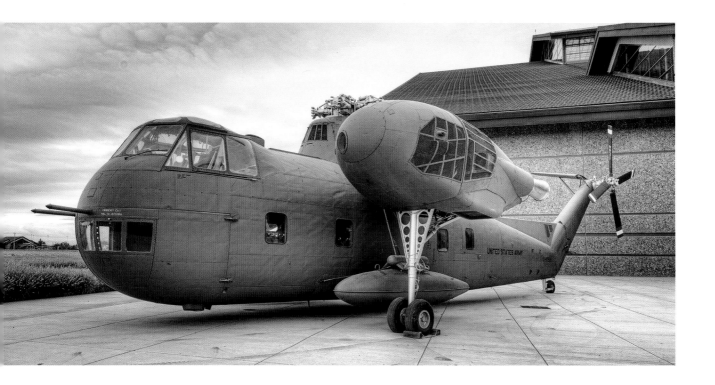

Sikorsky CH-37B *Mojave*

Specifications

The Korean War proved that the helicopter would be a large part of any future war and the U.S. Marine Corps wanted to make sure they had a troop transport helicopter with a heavy lift capacity. Sikorsky was asked to provide a solution and they created the S-56; the world's largest helicopter at the time. Given the designation HR2S by the Marines, the new craft featured twin piston engines mounted in side pods to make more room available in the fuselage for cargo and twin doors in the nose that would allow vehicles to be driven aboard.

The Army quickly became interested in the S-56 and bought 90 of the aircraft under the designation CH-37 *Mojave*. During the Vietnam War, four *Mojave*s were used to recover downed helicopters and aircraft. Although one was lost to enemy action, the *Mojave*s recovered over $7.5 million in equipment from behind enemy lines.

This CH-37B served with the 19th Transportation Company in Korea and was restored by the Museum's team in Marana, Arizona.

Type:	Cargo
First Flight:	1953
Rotorspan:	72 feet
Length:	64 feet, 3 inches
Height:	22 feet
Power:	Two Pratt & Whitney R-2800-54 Double Wasp radial engines
Crew:	3
Capacity:	26 troops or 24 stretchers
Top Speed:	130 miles per hour

ROTARY WING FLIGHT

Sikorsky H-19D *Chickasaw*

During the Korean War, the U.S. Army lacked helicopters with large payload capacity, and the Sikorsky H-19 helped to solve this problem. Designed throughout a span of seven months, it was a departure from earlier helicopters, with the engine located in the nose and the pilots up high to make room for more passengers or cargo.

So needed was the H-19 that the U.S. ordered more than 1,500, and Sikorsky was forced to license manufacture it in several countries to meet worldwide demand. Its innovative features included metallic rotor blades, shock absorbers on all the landing gear and maintenance without specialized tools. Entering operations in 1950, it was capable of moving ten troops or freight and was especially valuable for search and rescue and medical evacuation. H-19s were used by all of the U.S. armed forces and 35 other countries.

In 2003, Delford M. Smith placed this *Chickasaw* on loan to the Museum after purchasing it from aircraft collector Jack Lenhardt.

Specifications

Type:	Utility
First Flight:	November 10, 1949
Rotorspan:	53 feet
Length:	62 feet, 7 inches
Height:	13 feet, 4 inches
Power:	One Pratt & Whitney R-1340-57 radial engine
Crew:	2
Capacity:	12 troops or 8 litters
Top Speed:	112 miles per hour

ROTARY WING FLIGHT

Sikorsky HO3S-1G *Dragonfly*

A product of legendary helicopter manufacturer Igor Sikorsky, the HO3S is probably best known for its appearance in the movie *The Bridges at Toko-Ri*. The HO3S was the naval variant of the successful S-51; the first helicopter developed for both the military and civilian markets. Unlike its predecessors, the S-51 could carry three passengers or two stretchers for medical evacuation. Having proven its value in rescues during the Korean War, the U.S. Coast Guard acquired eight HO3S-1Gs between 1946 and 1950. They performed countless search and rescue

missions and were the first Coast Guard helicopters in the Great Lakes, helping to guide icebreakers through the frozen lakes.

This HO3S-1G was originally built as a civilian S-51 and was sold to Helicopter Air Transport (HAT); the first commercial helicopter company in the U.S. After HAT ceased operation, the aircraft was sold to the Coast Guard and modified for rescue work. It later went through several civilian owners before being restored to its Coast Guard configuration by Jack Lenhardt.

Specifications

Type:	Cargo / Rescue
First Flight:	August 18, 1943
Rotorspan:	48 feet
Length:	41 feet, 2 inches
Height:	12 feet, 11 inches
Power:	One Pratt & Whitney R-985 radial engine
Crew:	1
Capacity:	3 passengers or two litters
Top Speed:	90 miles per hour

ROTARY WING FLIGHT

Sikorsky UH-3H *Sea King*

Specifications

Developed for the U.S. Navy, the Sikorsky H-3 *Sea King* family of helicopters was designed around its ability to track and destroy submarines. Featuring a folding tail and rotor blades, the *Sea King* could operate from destroyers, as well as aircraft carriers, to provide protection to the fleet. It carried a "dipping" sonar to listen for submerged subs and homing torpedoes to make the kill if necessary.

Because of the H-3's boat-like hull, it could float on the water, making it a great vehicle for search and rescue work.

Its cabin capacity made it a good cargo hauler too. *Sea King*s transported the astronauts after most spaceflights in the 1960s and 70s, as well as serving the President of the United States as Marine One.

This *Sea King* last served with the U.S. Navy and is painted to resemble the Apollo 11 prime recovery helicopter. It is on loan from the National Museum of Naval Aviation.

Type:	Utility
First Flight:	March 11, 1959
Rotorspan:	62 feet
Length:	54 feet, 9 inches
Height:	16 feet, 10 inches
Power:	Two General Electric T58-GE-10 turboshaft engines
Crew:	4
Top Speed:	166 miles per hour

ROTARY WING FLIGHT

Sikorsky UH-34D *Seahorse*

The UH-34 began life as an enlarged version of Sikorsky's H-19 and incorporated many of its features, including a nose mounted engine and an elevated cockpit for more cargo space. Created for the U.S. Navy as an anti-submarine helicopter, the big, capable *Seahorse* quickly went into service with all branches of the U.S. military. A workhorse of the helicopter world, the UH-34 was one of the first truly reliable medium capacity helicopters and examples still fly today.

The Marine Corps was a very enthusiastic user of the UH-34 in Vietnam; as its reliability far exceeded other helicopters and it had the ability to absorb lots of combat damage. When the Marines replaced their *Seahorse*s in 1968, the remaining UH-34s were all turned over to the South Vietnamese Air Force (VNAF).

This UH-34D was one of those given to South Vietnam. Its unique history was discovered during restoration and the decision was made to restore it as it appeared during its service with the VNAF.

Specifications

Type:	Cargo
First Flight:	March 8, 1954
Rotorspan:	56 feet
Length:	56 feet, 8.5 inches
Height:	15 feet, 11 inches
Power:	One Wright R-1820-84 radial engine
Crew:	2
Capacity:	16 passengers or 8 stretchers
Top Speed:	123 miles per hour

ROTARY WING FLIGHT

Sikorsky S-61R

Specifications

The S-61R was developed by Sikorsky as a private venture to extend the usefulness of their successful H-3 *Sea King* series of helicopters. In the process, the S-61R received a longer fuselage with a rear loading ramp door and tricycle landing gear, while losing the "boat" hull of the H-3. The U.S. Air Force took notice of the new helicopter and ordered a number which they dubbed HH-3E "Jolly Green Giants." These machines were quickly put into service in Vietnam, being used for the rescue of pilots shot down behind enemy lines and support of special operations. The U.S. Coast Guard also bought the S-61R under the designation of HH-3F *Pelican*, and it served in the long range search and rescue role for over 30 years.

Because of its large capacity and range, the S-61R found numerous civilian users including Evergreen Helicopters, which used S-61Rs for heavy lift tasks such as construction and logging.

This S-61R is on loan from Evergreen Helicopters.

Type:	Cargo / Search & Rescue
First Flight:	June 17, 1963
Rotorspan:	62 feet
Length:	73 feet
Height:	18 feet, 1 inch
Power:	Two General Electric T58-110 turboshaft engines
Crew:	3
Capacity:	28 passengers
Top Speed:	165 miles per hour

ROTARY WING FLIGHT

AVIATION TIMELINE

1907   1936   1942   1946   1949

November 13, 1907

Paul Cornu makes the first piloted vertical take-off in a rotary-wing aircraft. He is lifted for 20 seconds at a height of 1 foot.

June 26, 1936

The German Focke-Wulf Fw 61, or Fa 61, becomes the first functional helicopter to fly.

January 13, 1942

The Sikorsky R-4 is the world's first large-scale mass-produced helicopter. It is also the first helicopter to enter service with the United States military.

March 8, 1946

Bell Helicopter's Bell 47 is the first helicopter certified for civilian use. Produced in several countries, the Bell 47, a two-bladed, single engine, light helicopter, will become the most popular helicopter model for nearly 30 years.

January 1949

The Hiller 360, later to be designated the Hiller OH-23 *Raven*, makes the first transcontinental flight, from California to New York, by a helicopter.

ROTARY WING FLIGHT

1956

1967

1975

1996

2007

October 22, 1956

The Bell UH-1 *Iroquois*, or Huey, makes its first flight. During the Vietnam conflict, the Huey will go under many modifications and upgrades to be tasked with transportation, ground attacks and armed escort roles.

April 7, 1967

Aérospatiale's *Gazelle* is the first helicopter to carry a Fenestron or fantail. This shrouding of the tail rotor reduces noise considerably.

September 30, 1975

Boeing AH-64 *Apache* completes its first flight. An attack helicopter, it will serve in many operations to accumulate more than 3 million flight hours. It will be the main assault aircraft for the U.S. Army in Iraq and Afghanistan.

January 4, 1996

The experimental Boeing/Sikorsky RAH-66 *Comanche* is the first stealth helicopter. With an all-composite five-blade main rotor and a special tail rotor assembly, the *Comanche's* noise signature is much smaller than others in its class. It also features radar-absorbent material, radar cross-section technology and infrared-suppressant paint.

June 13, 2007

The Bell-Boeing V-22 *Osprey*, a multi-mission, military, tiltrotor aircraft, is introduced. The *Osprey* is capable of both vertical take-off and landing (VTOL) and short take-off and landing (STOL). Its technology combines the functionality of a helicopter with the performance of a turboprop aircraft.

ROTARY WING FLIGHT

CAPTAIN MICHAEL KING SMITH
FIREARMS COLLECTION

EVERGREEN
AVIATION & SPACE
MUSEUM

FIREARMS COLLECTION

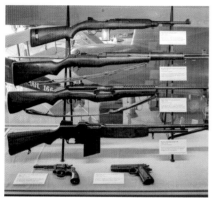

The Captain Michael King Smith Firearms Collection

In 2009, the Evergreen Aviation & Space Museum opened the Captain Michael King Smith Firearms Collection, a new exhibit located on the Aviation Museum mezzanine. This world-class collection of firearms from every era of American history occupies 18 cases and 4,000 square feet, overlooking Howard Hughes' massive *Spruce Goose*.

The Collection is brought to life by seven large-scale dioramas depicting Lewis and Clark's arrival at the Oregon coast, Teddy Roosevelt's Rough Riders at San Juan Hill, the Wild West, World War II in the Pacific, World War II over Europe, a 1950s boy's room and a sport hunting scene with a father and his son.

The Collection also includes a display on the Second Amendment, which illustrates how these artifacts are literally woven into the fabric of America from as far back as the founding fathers and the framers of our U.S. Constitution.

The National Firearms Museum in Fairfax, Virginia assisted the Museum in the preparation of the Collection in order to insure that only the finest, historically accurate artifacts are put on display for the public. Whether you are a firearm aficionado, an avid hunter, a history buff, a student or simply an interested onlooker, you will find something of interest in this tasteful tribute to the role that firearms have played in the rich history of the United States.

FIREARMS COLLECTION

Space Flight

While some people dreamed of soaring free like the birds, others dreamed of flying "beyond the sky" to the planets and the stars. Within 25 years of the Wright Brothers' first flight, the road to space was opened by Robert Goddard and his first liquid fueled rocket. After being used as a terrible weapon of war, the rocket became a tool of science and exploration, taking the first human beyond the Earth's atmosphere in 1961, and a mere eight years later, putting the first human on another heavenly body. When Neil Armstrong took his "One Small Step…" on the moon, mankind had forever left the cradle of its birth.

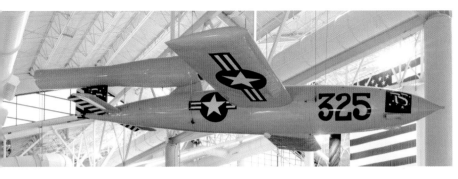

Dawn of the Space Age

The first step on the road to space took place not on the coast of Florida or the plains of Kazakhstan, but rather in a New England farm field. There, on March 16, 1926, a flimsy, tube-like structure built by Robert Goddard lifted off and flew 41 feet into the air. With this first successful liquid fuel rocket, the theories of visionaries like Konstantin Tsiolkovsky and Hermann Oberth came closer to reality and mankind closer to the stars.

But Goddard was not alone in developing rockets. In Germany, amateur experimenters had made great headway, and with the rise of the Third Reich, their talents were incorporated into Hitler's war machine. Under the leadership of Wernher von Braun, they were able to build the first rocket to reach space; the V-2. Only the V-2 was not designed for spaceflight, it was designed to rain explosives and terror down on civilian targets.

After World War II, the victors grabbed the spoils of war, including the V-2 and the scientists who built it. Used as a stepping stone, the V-2's technology would find its way into American missiles like the Redstone and Russian missiles like the R-7. These powerful rockets designed to carry nuclear warheads did, however, find a more peaceful mission; launching Earth orbiting satellites. On October 4, 1957, an R-7 rocket designed by Sergei Korolyov blasted *Sputnik I* into orbit, and brought the world firmly into the Space Age. Three months later, a Redstone missile designed by von Braun launched America's Explorer I, and the "space race" was on.

SPACE FLIGHT

First Humans in Space

On the morning of April 12, 1961, Soviet factories ground to a halt, buses and streetcars stopped rolling, and students abandoned their classes to listen to excited announcements on radios and public loudspeakers. At 9:07 a.m. Moscow time, cosmonaut Yuri Gagarin lifted off into space aboard Vostok (The East). One hour and 48 minutes later, after a single orbit of Earth, Gagarin and Vostok landed safely onto the "sacred soil of [the Soviet] motherland." Gagarin had flown higher (188 miles) and faster (18,000 m.p.h.) than anyone ever before. The centuries-old dream of humans in space had finally become a reality.

The U.S. had succeeded in launching a handful of satellites beginning with Explorer I in January of 1958. It had founded the National Aeronautics and Space Administration (NASA) later in 1958. Soon NASA established Project Mercury with the goal of launching the first man into space. But Gagarin's flight had stolen America's thunder.

Three weeks later, the U.S. launched its first man into space. On May 5, 1961, Freedom 7 with astronaut Alan Shepard aboard lifted off from Cape Canaveral, Florida, powered by a Redstone rocket. After a 15-minute flight that briefly lobbed the spacecraft into space before it plummeted back to Earth, Freedom 7 splashed down safely in the Atlantic Ocean. Compared to Gagarin's Earth-circling 1 hour and 48 minute flight, it was not much. But it was an exhilarating beginning. Twenty days later, President Kennedy set America's sights on the moon.

SPACE FLIGHT

Titan II

The development of the Intercontinental Ballistic Missile (ICBM) was the single greatest catalyst of the space race between the U.S. and the Soviet Union.

As the Cold War enemies stared each other down across the "Iron Curtain," they recalled the destructive lessons learned from World War II. Bombers could be shot down by fighters and anti-aircraft fire, but the missile remained unstoppable.

Both sides began to build missiles that could be launched at a moment's notice and deliver a knockout blow to the opponent using a nuclear warhead. To carry the large, heavy nuclear weapons over intercontinental distances, the missiles had to be extremely powerful. The ability to boost heavy payloads made them the perfect vehicles for launching capsules carrying humans into space. For the Russians, the R-7 missile, derived from the SS-6 *Sapwood* ICBM, was the basis for all their space launch vehicles, including the *Sputnik*, Vostok, Voskhod and Soyuz. On the American side, it was the Redstone,

Atlas and Titan that would carry the load in both war and peace.

Of the U.S. missiles, the Titan was the largest and most powerful of the group, and featured two stages with liquid fuel engines. The first version, the Titan I, was a silo-based ICBM built by the Glenn L. Martin Company that required fueling and being raised to the surface before it was launched. Needing a faster response time, the U.S. Air Force asked Martin to develop the Titan II, which could be kept fueled for long periods of time and would be ready

SPACE FLIGHT

to launch from the silo at the push of a button. This highly capable rocket was chosen to carry the two-man Gemini spacecraft into orbit.

The Titan II on display is the last variant of the Titan II family, the Space Launch Vehicle (SLV). On these missiles, the nuclear warhead was removed and a new fairing was adapted that could carry a satellite into orbit, or in one case, the *Clementine*, an unmanned space probe to the moon. A total of 14 Titan IIs were converted to this role by Martin-Marietta, and all but the Museum's

were used to launch satellites. Lacking a customer that required the Titan's lifting capacity, the missile was retired and turned over to the National Museum of the United States Air Force, who in turn loaned it to the Museum.

The Museum's Titan II is displayed in a launch position, with the white satellite fairing at its top. Down below, visitors can experience the control room that was used for the Titan II launches at Vandenburg Air Force Base, California. Complete down to the floor tiles, the control room allows visitors to

experience the last flight of a Titan II, which took place on October 17, 2003. It was gifted to the Museum by the Lockheed-Martin company.

SPACE FLIGHT

Project Gemini and Project Apollo

America was in space. Project Mercury had demonstrated reliable rocket performance and safe spacecraft design. The Mercury astronauts had shown that people could function in zero gravity. But, NASA knew it needed more information before humans could walk on the moon. Thus, Project Gemini was created. Its objective was to develop techniques for advanced space travel, which included new equipment, more control over spacecraft, and additional information about the effects of space travel on the human body.

At 8,400 pounds (compared to Mercury's 3,000 pounds) Gemini required a bigger and more powerful rocket than Atlas to lift it into orbit. NASA turned to the Air Force's newest, largest and most powerful ICBM, the Titan II. With its high power-to-weight ratio giving it blistering acceleration, the Titan II soon became the astronauts' favorite.

After 10 manned flights between 1965 and 1966, Project Gemini had successfully accomplished the first American spacewalks and new

maneuvers such as orbital rendezvous and docking. NASA was now prepared to embark on Project Apollo.

Project Apollo was named after the Greek and Roman sun god, patron of music and poetry, wisdom and truth. By 1967, six years after President Kennedy issued his mandate, the Apollo had become a gargantuan effort, dwarfing even World War II's atomic bomb-producing Manhattan Project. More than 400,000 people were working around the country to produce spaceships and rockets to carry U.S.

SPACE FLIGHT

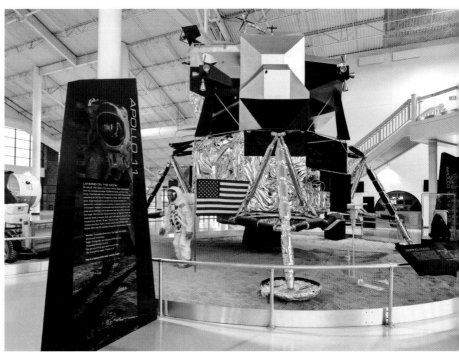

astronauts to the moon.

On December 21, 1968, astronauts Frank Borman, Jim Lovell and Bill Anders lifted off from Kennedy Space Center to venture where no human being had gone before. Since Yuri Gagarin's flight in 1961, 34 Soviet and American explorers had visited space but no further than 850 miles from the Earth's surface. But, Apollo 8 streaked toward the moon, some 230,000 miles away. Three days later on December 24, Apollo 8 settled into orbit around the moon, and just seven months

later, Buzz Aldrin and Neil Armstrong walked on the moon, establishing the Apollo program as one of the greatest technological achievements of all time.

The era of Apollo closed as it had begun, as a means to political ends. It was created to restore America's confidence and image worldwide and to beat the rival Soviets to the moon. It ended as a symbol of cooperation with that very rival. On July 17, 1975, with détente between the U.S. and Soviet Union in the air, and a treaty specifying arms reductions and increased human

rights about to be signed, an Apollo command module docked with an orbiting Soviet Soyuz spacecraft. While TV cameras provided live coverage, amidst welcoming messages from U.S. president Gerald Ford and Soviet leader Leonid Brezhnev, the beaming crews shook hands. The meeting not only provided a welcome thaw to the Cold War, it was a preview of the kind of cooperation necessary for the multi-national International Space Station to come.

SPACE FLIGHT

The Space Shuttle and International Space Station

The first shuttle orbiter, *Columbia*, flew into space on April 12, 1981, and it marked the debut of the world's first reusable spacecraft. The shuttle launches like a rocket, maneuvers in orbit like a spacecraft and lands like an airplane. It was designed to be a bus-like workhorse, ferrying people and materials into space, and it has largely succeeded, boosting more than 200 crewmembers and 3 million pounds of cargo into orbit.

Shuttle crews have included NASA astronauts; researchers from government, industry and universities; and scientists from many nations. Besides flying and maintaining the shuttle, these crews conduct research and experiments; launch, retrieve and repair satellites (including launching and later repairing the Hubble Space Telescope); and provide a lifeline to the International Space Station.

The Space Shuttle Program officially came to an end in July 2011, after flying 135 missions over 30 years.

Launched in 1998, and involving 16 nations—the U.S., Russia, Canada, Japan, Brazil and the 11 countries of the European Space Agency—the International Space Station (ISS) is one of the largest international co-operations ever attempted. Already the largest space station, the ISS continues to be assembled in orbit and more than 150 people representing some 18 nations have lived and worked there. Beyond the sheer technical brilliance and personal courage involved in building and sustaining the ISS, it is significant as an example of the powerful possibilities of global cooperation.

SPACE FLIGHT

Exploring the Planets

In the half-century since *Sputnik* first ascended to the heavens, we earthlings have embarked on more than 200 missions to explore the solar system. Humans have traveled into space on shuttles, orbited the Earth in space stations and walked on the moon.

But the vastness of space, and the expense involved in going there, has made further human exploration difficult. Robotic spacecraft, less expensive, less fragile and less needy than humans, have long been exploring where we have not yet gone. Robot

explorers have visited the sun and every planet in the solar system, as well as assorted moons, asteroids and comets. Two robotic travelers, *Voyager 1* and *Voyager 2*, are headed out of the solar system, the first human-made objects to foray into interstellar space. These robotic explorers are making discoveries that provide insights into the origins of the sun, planets and even life on Earth.

Leading the effort is NASA's Jet Propulsion Laboratory (JPL). Since their pioneering work on *Explorer I*, JPL has been building probes to

explore the unknown and some of the most exciting scientific discoveries of the last 50 years have come from these probes. Among the most famous are the Mars Exploration Rovers, *Spirit* and *Opportunity*, which together have been operating on Mars for over seven years. They are soon to be accompanied by an autonomous rover named Curiosity that will search for signs of past life on the red planet. Who knows what incredible things it will find.

SPACE FLIGHT

AVIATION TIMELINE

1926

1942

1957

1961

1963

March 16, 1926

Robert Goddard, an American professor, physicist and inventor, launches the first liquid fueled rocket, a milestone in bringing humans closer to spaceflight.

October 3, 1942

A product of Wernher von Braun's design, the Nazi V-2 rocket becomes the first vehicle to achieve sub-orbital spaceflight, reaching 62 miles from the Earth's surface, the boundary of space.

October 4, 1957

The Soviet Union's *Sputnik 1* is the first artificial satellite to be put into Earth's orbit. With its launch, the satellite marks the start of the Space Race between the United States and the Soviet Union.

April 12, 1961

Cosmonaut Yuri Gagarin is the first human to journey into outer space, when his Vostok spacecraft completes an orbit of the Earth.

June 16, 1963

Valentina Tereshkova, a Soviet cosmonaut, is the first woman in space, piloting Vostok 6.

SPACE FLIGHT

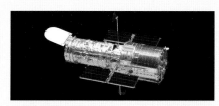

1969

1981

1990

2000

2004

July 21, 1969

During the Apollo 11 mission, Americans Neil Armstrong and Buzz Aldrin are the first men to step onto Earth's moon.

April 12, 1981

NASA's Space Shuttle is the first reusable manned orbital spacecraft. Serving on 135 missions, the shuttle program will launch numerous satellites, interplanetary probes, conduct science experiments in space and assist in construction of the International Space Station.

April 24, 1990

The Hubble Space Telescope (HST) is one of the largest and most versatile space telescopes. Orbiting outside of the distortion of Earth's atmosphere, HST will be able to take very detailed images with almost no background light. Many of its observations will lead to breakthroughs in astrophysics, such as determining the rate of the universe's expansion.

November 2, 2000

Astronaut Bill Shepherd and cosmonauts Yuri Gidzenko and Sergei Krikalev of Expedition One are the first people to take up residence at the International Space Station (ISS). ISS is an internationally-developed research facility and the largest space station constructed.

January 4, 2004

A free ranging rover, *Spirit*, lands on Mars to analyze the geology of the planet's rocks and planetary surface features.

SPACE FLIGHT

Special Programs and Places of Interest

Education

At the Evergreen Aviation & Space Museum, we have a passion for education and are committed to creating and offering the best educational programming available. Our current roster of programs drives home the importance we place on "inspiring and educating." Not only do we offer rigorous instruction in the mathematic and scientific fields, we also present students with the opportunity to put the skills they learn into practice. A few of the programs we provide are home school events, summer camps, Boy Scout merit badge classes, book clubs, educational outreach and the Engineering Aerospace and Science Academy (EASA) in conjunction with McMinnville High School, as well as many other educational opportunities throughout the year.

Development

The Evergreen Aviation & Space Museum was a gift to the community and aviation world from Evergreen International Aviation's owner and founder, Delford M. Smith, and his son, Captain Michael King Smith. Today, we can operate because of the generosity of our members, donors and charitable foundations. The Museum accepts donations in the form of cash, checks, stocks, bonds, pledges and other liquid commodities. We are also thankful to those who include us in their wills and charitable remainder trusts.

Membership

Museum members are an important aspect of the team that ensures

MUSEUM PROGRAMS

Special Programs and Places of Interest

the Museum's continued growth and success. Along with the board of directors, volunteers, staff and community supporters, our members are critical to fulfilling our mission *to inspire and educate, to promote and preserve aviation and space history, and to honor the patriotic service of our veterans.*

All Museum members receive unlimited free admission to the Aviation and Space Museums; a discount on movies; free access to more than 250 museums worldwide through the Association of Science-Technology Centers (ASTC); a one-year subscription to the *Wingspan* newsletter; invitations to exclusive members-only events; a 10 percent discount on purchases at the Museum gift stores; discounts on educational camps, classes and lectures; and free access to the Captain Michael King Smith Firearms Collection.

Special Events

The Evergreen Aviation & Space Museum campus offers a unique opportunity to hold your event in your choice of expansive and elegant steel and glass facilities with floor-to-ceiling windows. The Museum's rental capacity is one of the largest in Oregon, with two buildings boasting over 120,000 square feet. Both the Aviation and Space Museum can accommodate up to 3,000 people for standing events and 1,500 people when seating is required. The Evergreen Theater offers not only theater seating and movie screening options for 232 people, but also several meeting and conference rooms. Outdoor venues such as the beautiful Jankowski Oak Grove and the West Patio are also available. The Evergreen

Aviation & Space Museum campus is a perfect location for your wedding, reunion, corporate meeting, convention or holiday party.

Evergreen Theater

Visitors to the Evergreen Aviation & Space Museum have the opportunity to experience state-of-the-art technology while viewing spectacular films. Featuring images that appear six stories high on a screen rising 53 feet tall and 70 feet wide, with sound delivered through a powerful digital audio system, you will feel more like a participant than a viewer. Add to the excitement of your visit to the Museum, and immerse yourself in a film environment real enough to reach out and touch.

Oregon Aviation Hall of Honor and Veteran Memorials

The Museum is home to the Oregon Aviation Hall of Honor, which inducts exceptional Oregonians annually for their outstanding contributions and achievements in the field of aviation and airpower. In keeping with the Museum mission to honor the patriotic service of our veterans, the Museum is also home to the Blue Star Memorial and the Purple Heart Memorial, as well as the Patriot Plaza near the Evergreen Theater.

The Museum Collections

The Museum's permanent collection includes aircraft, spacecraft, library and archive materials, art and photographs and an impressive uniform collection that encompasses commercial and military service wear. The Museum actively collects artifacts that not only

MUSEUM PROGRAMS

Special Programs and Places of Interest

pay tribute to our veterans, but also educate and inspire achievement in our youth. Museum professionals carefully preserve artifacts for use in educational programs, temporary and permanent exhibits and for scholarly research. The Museum's library and archive collection contains more than 6,000 books, periodicals and other published and unpublished materials, many items of which are irreplaceable.

Cafés

The Spruce Goose Café and *Cosmo Café*

offer gourmet fare made fresh daily, including sandwiches, burgers, soups and salads. Fountain drinks, coffee and tea are available to quench your thirst. You can visit the Cafés without paying admission to the general exhibit space and still enjoy the atmosphere of the Museum.

Evergreen Farm Stores

Stop by the Evergreen Farm Stores, with locations in the Aviation Museum and Space Museum, for gourmet treats or wine tasting. The Farm Stores are open

seven days a week and do not require paid admission to the Museum.

Gift Stores

Pick up a souvenir at *Rotors, Wings & Things* in the Aviation Museum or *The Right Stuff* in the Space Museum. Find a unique selection of model aircraft, history books, space souvenirs, educational toys, clothing and one-of-a-kind gifts. Visiting the gift stores does not require paid admission to the Museums.

MUSEUM PROGRAMS

RC Aircraft Flight Field

The Museum operates a Remote Control (RC) Aircraft Flight Field in partnership with the Evergreen Aero Modelers. RC modeling is an exciting sport with highly detailed airplanes that look surprisingly real and can cost thousands of dollars to build. RC aircraft events promise to be an exciting part of the Museum experience that the whole family can enjoy.

Restoration

The Evergreen Aviation & Space

Museum takes pride in the quality restoration of our aircraft. A crew of skilled volunteers has carefully restored many of the aircraft seen in the Museum today, such as the Hughes' *Flying Boat*, SR-71 *Blackbird* and Douglas A-26C *Invader*, among others.

Volunteers

Special thanks to the volunteers who have been crucial to the growth of the Evergreen Aviation & Space Museum. Docents are always available to answer questions and give tours, as well as

provide support and expertise to every area of the Museum, including restoration, education, special events, artifact cataloging and preservation, exhibit installation, administration, community outreach, and retail and membership sales.

Our volunteers are an integral part of the educational power of our Museum. Whether you are an aviation fan or a veteran of flight, we welcome you to join our enthusiastic team of volunteers.

MUSEUM PROGRAMS

Evergreen Wings & Waves Waterpark

Opened June 2011, Evergreen Wings & Waves is the newest addition to the Evergreen Aviation & Space Museum campus. The first waterpark of its kind, Wings & Waves is designed to create an environment that not only teaches the public about aircraft, but also demonstrates the importance of skills like mathematics, science, teamwork, determination and perseverance. The addition of the Waterpark adds another layer of education, teaching families about the power and importance of water.

The facility features more than 70,000-square-feet (or one and one quarter football fields) of educational fun, highlighted by a massive Evergreen International Aviation Boeing 747 aircraft that rests on the top of the building with four waterslides coming off either side to carry swimmers over the roof and into the water below. The pool temperature, at 84 degrees, is powered by six natural gas heaters.

The Waterpark houses 10 waterslides and a large wave pool that holds more than 91,000 gallons of water. A special area is dedicated to toddlers with bubblers, fountains and two slides. Plus, a play structure that includes a 300 gallon splash bucket and helicopter. And for the older kid in the group, a leisure pool with spa and vortex pool.

Other features include an interactive hands-on science center; the *Starcade* gaming center and gift store for on-land fun; the *Milky Way Café*, a concession area to keep swimmers energized; private rooms available to reserve for birthday parties or other celebrations; and family-style locker rooms.

CAMPUS EXPANSION

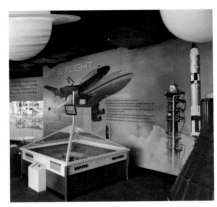

The Nation's Only Educational Waterpark

Throughout the Waterpark visitors learn about the power of water and its effects on society through dozens of interactive exhibits and learning tools. Both the Museum and the Waterpark aim to serve an important community education role and further distinguish McMinnville as a premier location for teaching students of all ages about the wonder of science.

H2O Hands-On Science Center

Designed to teach visitors about the philosophy, "Life Needs Water," the *H2O Hands-On Science Center* has over 20 educational interactive exhibits. Visitors will learn how to create enough pressure to launch a rocket, sail a ship down the Columbia river, or climb into an interactive submarine sailing through the deep blue seas.

Following Oregon State Standards, each exhibit educates visitors on the scientific benefits of water. One of the largest interactive exhibits in the Science Center, the Life Needs Water exhibit teaches students how the hydrologic cycle affects our planet and how and where humans and animals live and survive. With visitor activated rain clouds integrated with another exhibit, the water cycle, this interactive gives the visitor the ability to touch the water and see it flow into the river.

Life Needs Water helps students analyze evidence for geologic, climatic, environmental, and life form changes over time. Among other lessons, they will understand how human activities are affected by the physical environment.

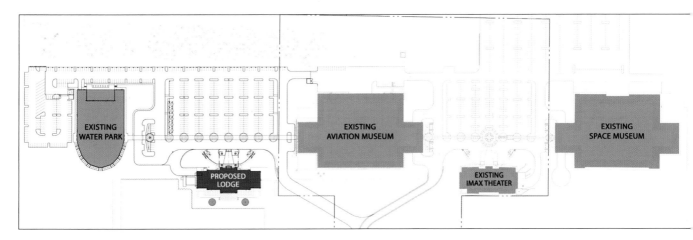

Evergreen Redhawk Lodge

The Museum campus expansion continues with the construction of the 5-story Evergreen Redhawk Lodge in 2012.

Designed in the style reminiscent of Works Project Administration lodges of the 1930s, it will feature 94 guest rooms, a distinctive lobby and seating area with a large wood burning fireplace.

Located between the Aviation Museum and Waterpark, the building will also remain consistent with Evergreen design. Beautiful views of the Evergreen

Vineyards and the Jankowski Oak Grove will surround a signature restaurant, a luxurious spa and a 24-hour fitness center.

The Lodge design features aviation and space-related themes in its architecture and interior design, and provides educational opportunities throughout the facility to learn about the wonder of flight. The theme of flight is carried through to different levels of the Lodge, as well as in the rooms and suites.

This newest construction will add

a much-needed dimension to the Evergreen Campus by allowing people to stay on-site and enjoy not only the Museum, Waterpark, and theater, but also provide quick access to McMinnville's historic downtown.

Like the Waterpark, the Lodge will have close ties to the Aviation and Space Museums. With education and inspiration at the forefront of our mission, we want visitors to see these elements present throughout the full campus experience.

CAMPUS EXPANSION

PHOTOGRAPHY CREDITS

Bill Bane

Paul Carter

Jim Collaboratoron

Rusty Denham

P. Alejandro Díaz

Jason Dodge

Pete Eckert

Julie Green

Konrad Korzen

Chris Ludwick

Aleksander Milewski

Dmitry A. Mottl

Allan Mullen

NASA

John Ousterhout

Adrian Pingstone

Don Pyle

Even Quach

Joe Stevens

Mark Toal

Dave Tripp

Dan Tyrpak

U.S. Library of Congress

Charlie Van Pelt

Rolf Wallner

David Yakimec

The Evergreen Aviation & Space Museum Guidebook
©2011 Evergreen Aviation & Space Museum

Evergreen would like to sincerely thank and acknowledge the following people who contributed significantly to this book: Delford M. Smith, Blythe Berselli, Robert Zeh, and the Evergreen team who built this company into what it is today.

For additional information, contact Evergreen International Aviation, Corporate Communications Department, 3850 Three Mile Lane, McMinnville, OR 97128.

Written and edited by Stewart W. Bailey.
Designed by Angela Van Grunsven.

ISBN:0-9776374-2-5
Tenth Anniversary Edition